PSYCHOLOGY PRACTITIONER GUIDEBOOKS

EDITORS

Arnold P. Goldstein, Syracuse University
Leonard Krasner, Stanford University & SUNY at Stony Brook
Sol L. Garfield, Washington University in St. Louis

PREVENTING RELAPSE IN THE ADDICTIONS

Pergamon Titles of Related Interest

Agras EATING DISORDERS: Management of Obesity, Bulimia and Anorexia Nervosa

Ellis/McInerney/DiGiuseppe/Yeager RATIONAL-EMOTIVE THERAPY WITH ALCOHOLICS AND SUBSTANCE ABUSERS

Hester/Miller HANDBOOK OF ALCOHOLISM TREATMENT APPROACHES: Effective Alternatives

Mermelstein SMOKING CESSATION: A Biopsychosocial Approach

Rhodes/Jason PREVENTING SUBSTANCE ABUSE AMONG CHILDREN AND ADOLESCENTS

Thompson BODY IMAGE DISTURBANCE: Assessment and Treatment

Weiss/Katzman/Wolchik TREATING BULIMIA: A Psychoeducational Approach

Williamson ASSESSMENT OF EATING DISORDERS: Obesity, Anorexia and Bulimia Nervosa

Related Journals
(Free sample copies available upon request)

ADDICTIVE BEHAVIORS: An International Journal
ALCOHOL
ALCOHOL AND ALCOHOLISM
ANNUAL REVIEW OF ADDICTIONS RESEARCH AND
   TREATMENT
CLINICAL PSYCHOLOGY REVIEW
JOURNAL OF SUBSTANCE ABUSE TREATMENT

PREVENTING RELAPSE IN THE ADDICTIONS
A Biopsychosocial Approach

EMIL J. CHIAUZZI

Northeast Psychiatric Associates and
Brookside Hospital, Nashua, NH

PERGAMON PRESS

Member of Maxwell Macmillan Pergamon Publishing Corporation
New York • Oxford • Beijing • Frankfurt
São Paulo • Sydney • Tokyo • Toronto

Pergamon Press Offices:

U.S.A.	Pergamon Press, Inc., Maxwell House, Fairview Park, Elmsford, New York 10523, U.S.A.
U.K.	Pergamon Press plc, Headington Hill Hall, Oxford OX3 0BW, England
PEOPLE'S REPUBLIC OF CHINA	Pergamon Press, Xizhimenwai Dajie, Beijing Exhibition Centre, Beijing 100044, China
GERMANY	Pergamon Press GmbH, Hammerweg 6, D-6242 Kronberg, Germany
BRAZIL	Pergamon Editora Ltda, Rua Eça de Queiros, 346, CEP 04011, Paraiso, São Paulo, Brazil
AUSTRALIA	Pergamon Press Australia Pty Ltd., P.O. Box 544, Potts Point, NSW 2011, Australia
JAPAN	Pergamon Press, 8th Floor, Matsuoka Central Building, 1-7-1 Nishishinjuku, Shinjuku-ku, Tokyo 160, Japan
CANADA	Pergamon Press Canada Ltd., Suite 271, 253 College Street, Toronto, Ontario M5T 1R5, Canada

Library of Congress Cataloging in Publication Data

Chiauzzi, Emil J., 1954–
    Preventing relapse in the addictions : a biopsychosocial approach / by Emil J. Chiauzzi.
      p.   cm. -- (Psychology practitioner guidebooks.)
    Includes bibliographical references and index.
    ISBN 0-08-037919-2 : -- ISBN
0-08-037918-4
    1. Substance abuse--Relapse--Prevention. 2. Substance abuse--Relapse--Prevention--Psychological aspects. 3. Substance abuse--Relapse--Prevention--Social aspects. I. Title. II. Series
    [DNLM: 1. Models, Biological. 2. Models, Psychological. 3. Risk Factors. 4. Substance Dependence--prevention & control.
5. Substance Dependence--psychology. 6. Substance Dependence--rehabilitation.   WM 270 C532p]
RC564.C49 1991
616.86′06--dc20
DNLM/DLC
for Library of Congress   90-14336
                                              CIP

Printing: 1 2 3 4 5 6 7 8 9 Year: 1 2 3 4 5 6 7 8 9 0

The paper used in this publication meets the minimum requirements of American National Standard for Information Sciences—Permanence of Paper for Printed Library Materials, ANSI Z39.48-1984

Contents

Preface

In my treatment and research in the field of addictions, I have often wondered how an experience as common as relapse could be so ignored. The mere mention of *relapse* can create anxiety in patients. Counselors, psychologists, social workers, and psychiatrists generally spend little time addressing relapse prevention, even though it is the overriding goal of treatment. In addition, I have been genuinely dismayed that there is so little cross-fertilization between fields. Psychological research that is potentially valuable in addictions treatment is often unfamiliar to frontline treatment professionals. I believe that these trends are counterproductive and can result in poor outcomes for alcoholics and addicts in treatment.

This book is aimed at bridging these gaps. The information contained in the following chapters has been gathered in the course of treating over 1,500 addicted individuals and conducting in-depth interviews with over 100 relapsers. In collecting this information, I have sought to balance clinical observations with empirical findings—the addictions field is often guilty of making conclusions in the absence of scientific fact. This book is organized around a *biopsychosocial* model and reviews empirically validated risk factors, assessments, and treatments that are pertinent to relapse. I have attempted to answer three questions: (a) What are the biological, psychological, and social risk factors for relapse? (b) How does one assess biological, psychological, and social risk factors for an individual patient? (c) What biological, psychological, and social interventions decrease the risk of relapse?

It is my hope that the result is a comprehensive guide to relapse prevention that can be applied in all addiction treatment settings. Professionals and students interested in learning about relapse prevention should find this book useful in expanding the scope of their assessment and intervention. In a broader sense, I also hope that this book encourages others to question traditional models of addiction treatment and to develop more creative and comprehensive interventions.

I would like to add that this book could not have been completed without the support of my friends and colleagues. I am especially indebted to Steve Liljegren, Ph.D., and Kathy Menne, M.S.W., for their helpful comments about the manuscript. Writing can sometimes be a singleminded experience that requires input from the "outside world." I would also like to thank Denise Bedard for her assistance in locating many of the references in this book. Finally, I owe many thanks to my friends and patients in recovery—I have learned more from you than you realize.

Introduction

For as long as mankind has been using drugs and alcohol, there have been numerous attempts to control or eliminate addiction. For many years, addicted people have tried heroic, extreme, and sometimes dangerous methods to free themselves from their drug of choice. Substituting one drug for another has always been the first thought of the addicted person in distress. Musto (1987) notes that "cures" for opium addiction in the late 1800s often involved ingestion of other opium-containing substances. Sigmund Freud reportedly gave cocaine to his good friend Ernst Fleischl von Markow in the hopes of curing the latter's morphine habit. This apparently benevolent act resulted in Fleischl's developing a major cocaine addiction and led to his death in 1891 (Sulloway, 1979). Another replacement for morphine, "heroin," was so named because it was thought to have "heroic" powers in curing morphine abuse (Freeman, 1988). Heroin was then found to be addictive and required its own treatment. Clinical researchers later developed methadone, now regarded as an abused drug in its own right (Bratter, Pennacchia, & Gauya, 1985).

"Geographical cures" are also frequently used by the desperate addict, who attempts to escape the grip of the addictive substance by vacationing or moving to a new locale. In the early 1900s, William Halstead, considered the "Father of American Surgery," attempted to stop his addictive use of cocaine by sailing to the Windward Islands (Phillips & Wynne, 1980). This geographical change resulted in a poor outcome, as he relapsed soon after his return. He ultimately died an active morphine addict in 1922.

The "willpower" approach has been advocated by religious groups and temperance organizations whose members preach that the addictive qualities of alcohol can easily overpower the unsuspecting user. Several years ago, this approach made a return as Nancy Reagan's "Just Say No" campaign. Unfortunately, many addicts and alcoholics can testify to the difficulty of applying this technique over long spans of time.

These relapse anecdotes are more than historical oddities. Despite the expansion of the substance abuse treatment industry, relapse rates remain unacceptably high (Peele, 1990). The trend continues, despite the flood of self-help books and expansion of organizations devoted to informing and treating addicts and their families. There is a fragmentation of the substance abuse treatment field, with a lack of communication between alcoholism counselors, psychologists, psychiatrists, social workers, and the recovering community. In the midst of all this, individuals seeking to recover from their addictions are underserved because of treatment models that are not comprehensive or flexible.

Substance abuse researchers have increasingly begun relying on *biopsychosocial* explanations of addiction (Donovan, 1988; Zucker & Gomberg, 1986). Theories that postulate single biological, psychological, or social causes for addiction are now considered to be overly simplistic. Even strong advocates of the disease concept admit that there are powerful psychological and social factors that can lead to expression of a predisposition for alcoholism (Goodwin, 1988). Schuckit (1984), who suggests that children of alcoholics have a diminished sensitivity to the effects of alcohol, also states, "It is unlikely there is a single cause for alcoholism. . . . At best, biologic factors explain only a part of [it]" (p. 883). Cloninger, Bohman, and Sigvardsson (1981), who discovered two major types of biologically transmitted alcoholism, wrote, "The demonstration of the critical importance of sociocultural influences in most alcoholics suggests that major changes in social attitudes about drinking styles can change dramatically the prevalence of alcohol abuse regardless of genetic predisposition" (p. 867).

The biopsychosocial perspective is especially useful for relapse prevention because it encourages relapsers to evaluate mistakes made in different areas of their lives. Many current explanations for relapse are simplistic and do not encourage the individual to explore errors made prior to the relapse. There are several common explanations: "I stopped going to A.A. meetings"; "I found myself with a drink in my hand"; "I guess I didn't hit my bottom"; and "I wanted to do it *my* way." Traditional approaches suggest that relapse arises from denial and that treatment should be repeated. Not surprisingly, the relapses are often repeated, too. Rather than learning from mistakes, the relapser becomes frustrated and passive, hoping for a spiritual awakening. This book examines active approaches that can provide hope and build the skills necessary for avoiding relapse.

The following chapters will address a variety of topics in the field of relapse prevention in an effort to provide clinicians and recovering persons with a framework for maintaining abstinence. Chapter 1 reviews current research on relapse rates. Among professionals and laymen alike, there are many perceptions about these rates. In addition, marketing departments in substance abuse treatment centers muddy the waters with poorly designed outcome studies—some even claiming 90% "success" rates. The data that I review suggest that these claims are questionable at best. I also discuss spontaneous remission rates, as it is important to learn from those who stop substance abuse on their own.

Chapter 2 discusses the myths that relapsers often harbor about the recovery process. These inaccurate beliefs can often increase the likelihood of relapse and should be reviewed with all individuals in early recovery.

Chapter 3 reviews different models of relapse prevention. Each of these models provides a useful viewpoint that can be incorporated into a biopsychosocial model. In comparing these techniques, I focus on the advantages of a comprehensive biopsychosocial approach.

Chapter 4 reviews research findings of biological, psychological, and social predictors of relapse. Current relapse literature does not fully address the assessment and treatment implications of sensation seeking, cue reactivity, and psychopathology. As treatment involves a significant psychoeducational component, accounting for cognitive dysfunction is also important. Factors such as personality structure and expectancy may mediate stress management in recovery. Social skills factors have been discussed in past literature, but it is clear that larger social issues such as unemployment and residential stability need to be assessed. Finally, this chapter addresses issues of treatment adherence and motivation as predictors of relapse.

Chapter 5 describes a comprehensive assessment that is based on a biopsychosocial risk analysis. An analysis of this kind includes evaluation of health factors, cognitive and behavioral skills, and relationship issues. Different types of relapse prevention and psychometric assessments are discussed.

Chapter 6 describes psychotherapeutic techniques for increasing self-efficacy, coping with craving, eliminating cognitive distortions, and building communication skills. The concept of family and couples relapse prevention is also reviewed, since "enabling" behaviors of significant others can help precipitate relapse.

Chapter 7 delineates relapse prevention issues with special populations—adolescents, women, the elderly, and impaired professionals. In addition to global concerns in relapse prevention, each population has particular challenges in recovery, for example, peer pressure in adolescents, dependency in females, fatalism in the elderly, and intellectualization and denial in impaired professionals.

Chapter 8 addresses specific addictions in relation to relapse prevention.

Drugs such as cocaine and nicotine, with their high addictive potential, present particular difficulties in recovery. Behaviors such as spending and gambling can seem innocuous but often continue compulsive patterns that may ultimately lead to relapse.

We begin with a review of methodology and outcome in addiction research.

Chapter 1

The Problem of Relapse

> *To think that I am not going*
> *to think of you any more*
> *is still thinking of you.*
> *Let me then try not to think*
> *that I am not going to think of you.*
> *—Zen saying*

The body of outcome research in alcoholism and other addictions is voluminous, but it is difficult to evaluate because of changes in definitions of alcoholism, differences in theoretical perspectives, and criteria for success. There are, however, discernible patterns in the timing of relapses and the similarity among addictions. This chapter offers a review of methodological problems in outcome research and a comparison of relapse rates among treatment settings and addictions.

METHODOLOGICAL ISSUES

Definitions of Relapse and Recovery

A colleague once told me, "Relapse is a dirty word. People don't want to talk about it." It is almost as if the very mention of the word will increase the likelihood of its occurrence. It is unthinkable, yet it is in the back of everyone's mind. We can all agree that relapse is a part of addiction, but it is seldom regarded as a topic in its own right. As in suicide prevention, those who rely on blissful ignorance often become statistics.

Despite the ubiquity of the phenomenon, there is little agreement as to what constitutes a relapse. Litman, Stapleton, Oppenheim, Peleg, and Jackson (1983) suggest that relapse can be regarded in five ways:

1. as a *discrete event* that is initiated with a return to substance use
2. as a *process* that insidiously leads to the initiation of substance use
3. as a return to the *same intensity* of substance use
4. as *daily use* for a specific number of sequential days
5. as a *consequence* of substance use, that is, requiring readmission for treatment

Determinations of successful outcome are highly dependent on one's definition of relapse. The most extreme definition would regard a relapse as *any* use of a mind-altering substance. Such a definition would place the actual use of the substance at the center of consideration. Inherent in this viewpoint is the notion that once the alcoholic individual returns to drinking, he or she immediately loses control (to the point of total relapse). Little attention is paid to other factors in recovery if the recovery does not meet the minimum criterion of abstinence. If this relapse occurs after a treatment, the treatment would be considered a failure. The relapser would need to begin recovery again. Repeated relapses could be regarded as evidence of poor motivation, as the relapser should understand the simple fact that substance use needs to be avoided.

At the other extreme, one would consider the actual substance use secondary to other circumstances in the person's life. The use of substances is symptomatic of underlying personality dynamics or stressors. Exploring these underlying causes can free the person from unseen negative forces. The substance abuser would then have no reason to use drugs because the *real* cause of such negative behavior would have been found. The focus would then be placed on psychological, social, work, and recreational functioning. The outcome is not measured in the amount of substance used, but in the *quality of life.*

Anyone familiar with substance abuse treatment will recognize the first definition as a hard-line version of the abstinence-oriented approach. The second definition represents the viewpoint of many insight-oriented psychotherapists. It is no wonder that these two camps have clashed over the years.

There has been mutual distrust between proponents of these philosophies. The result has been that the recovering substance abuser was short-changed. Many alcoholics who sought psychotherapy found that there was implicit approval of drinking because many therapists did not focus on it directly. As a result, drinking continued and the openness and honesty necessary for productive therapy did not develop. Outcome literature suggests that traditional psychotherapy has been generally ineffective in treating alcoholism and drug addiction (Baekland, 1977).

On the other hand, many alcoholics in recovery have found that "not drinking was not enough." Sobriety does not automatically resolve all problems, as is implied by extreme versions of the abstinence-oriented message. Individuals with personality problems, psychiatric diagnoses, poor coping skills, or psychosocial stress often relapse after trying simple abstinence. Focusing on abstinence from one substance or behavior can also detract from the potentially deleterious effects of other substitute addictions. These deficiencies can harm treatment and, as a result, the outcome for traditional substance abuse programs is mixed at best (Miller & Hester, 1986).

Most contemporary treatments of substance abuse attempt to achieve a combination of abstinence and self-knowledge. A commitment to absolute abstinence has been found to reduce the possibility of relapse (Hall, Havassy, & Wasserman, 1990). Many experts in the field consider abstinence to be an important prerequisite to meaningful recovery, especially as there are no treatment programs that can reliably teach chronic alcoholics to drink moderately (Nathan & Skinstad, 1987). As Vaillant (1983) states, "It must be remembered that abstinence is a means, not an end. It is justifiable as a treatment goal only if moderate drinking is not an alternative and only if sight is not lost of the real goal—social rehabilitation" (p. 215). Alcoholics Anonymous (A.A.) has long differentiated between being *sober* and being *dry*. The former term is reserved for those who have achieved a reasonable level of self-understanding, while the latter term refers to those who have simply stopped drinking while continuing other negative behaviors.

There are other potentially harmful effects of the conflict between these viewpoints. The negation of controlled drinking alternatives by advocates of the disease model has also led to the repudiation of many behavioral techniques that could be used to move toward abstinence goals. Among these are social-skills training, stress inoculation training, stress management techniques, cognitive therapy, anger control treatments, self-monitoring, and aversion techniques. Traditional substance abuse treatments often use unsystematic versions of these methods and could benefit from the research and standardization developed by behavioral researchers. In addition, an appreciation of research methodology could lead to a cross-fertilization of these approaches and potentially result in more effective treatments.

There is also a need to consider the point at which relapse begins. Many recovering people who attempt to use a previously abused substance assume that they will lose control. This can create a self-fulfilling prophecy (Marlatt, 1985a). In my experience, many relapsed alcoholics and addicts began with controlled usage and gradually moved to more chronic usage. This progression requires a refinement in the definition of relapse. Does it occur at the first instance of substance use? Does it involve intoxication? Can it occur after one day of abstinence?

In this regard, it is helpful to utilize Marlatt's (1985b) distinction between *lapse* and *relapse.* He considers the former a *slip* (as does A.A.) or
mistake. The latter can be regarded as a more significant deterioration or
backsliding. This distinction has ramifications for treatment, since amelio-
ration (rather than perfect abstinence) becomes the primary goal (McAuliffe et al., 1986). In what other area of medical treatment is an outcome
that falls short of perfection viewed as a failure? We can reach for the goal
of abstinence, but the experience of recovering addicts suggests that the
occurrence of relapse is almost universal. Indeed, many experts in the field
have regarded relapse as a *defining characteristic* of addiction (Lindesmith,
1968).

Patient Selection Issues

In addition to inadequate definitions of relapse, there are three patient
selection issues that often prevent clear interpretation of results: (a) treatment dropouts, (b) population bias, and (c) poor follow-up procedures. In
terms of treatment dropouts, patients who complete treatment are three
times more likely to be abstinent 1 year later than are those who do not
complete treatment (Baekland & Lundwall, 1975). Unfortunately, the statistical analyses of many treatment programs evaluate only treatment
completers, thus inflating success estimates (Nathan & Skinstad, 1987). For
a treatment to be truly successful, it should be able to retain as many
admissions as possible.

There has been a history of highly confrontational treatment in the
substance abuse field. One recovering alcoholic and cocaine addict described her treatment at a long-term treatment center in the 1970s. She told
me, "I had to crawl on my hands and knees to beg the therapist not to kick
me out of treatment. I wore pajamas with a sign 'I'm a sick baby dope fiend
and I don't know anything.' " Not surprisingly, she later relapsed. Other
patients treated at some therapeutic communities report incidents such as
cleaning floors with toothbrushes and wearing self-derogatory signs.

While such reports are extreme, one can also assume that any person
who endures this type of highly confrontational treatment is also highly
motivated. Trying to generalize the outcome of these programs from such
a limited sample will only obscure the large number of people who left
before completion. As a result, the treatment will appear successful when
it frequently is not. Confrontation may simply weed out the people who
cannot tolerate intense feedback, leaving the "cream of the crop," that is,
those who are so motivated that they would benefit from any treatment.

Follow-up procedures are also problematic. This is especially apparent
in the marketing procedures of many private hospitals seeking to convince
the public that they have "the answer." Several years ago, I heard of an

outcome report released by a private substance abuse treatment center. This facility sent out questionnaires to all persons who had completed the treatment program. The number of questionnaires sent out was not reported—only the number of respondents: 260. They were asked, "Are you still drinking?" and 91% replied "no." Seventy-five percent reported total abstinence since leaving and 97% were involved with A.A. Since alcoholics who are difficult to locate at follow-up are more likely to relapse (Moos & Bliss, 1978), it is not surprising that the response to this questionnaire was so favorable.** Follow-up rates are often not given in such outcome reports.

To make an accurate assessment of success is also difficult with follow-up periods shorter than 2 years. The "natural history" of alcoholism is unstable and includes remissions, nonproblem drinking, and relapses (Nathan & Skinstad, 1987). Most studies use 3-month, 6-month, and 1-year follow-ups. Longer follow-up periods are necessary to establish a more significant trend.

Relapse Curves

No book on relapse would be complete without the relapse curve presented and explained by Hunt, Barnett, and Branch (1971) (Figure 1.1). Their review is perhaps the most widely cited two-page article in behavioral psychology and is often used to illustrate the commonalities in relapse between addictions. The meaning of this graph is clear: Approximately 60% of heroin, alcohol, and smoking relapses occur within the first 3 months. There is a negative acceleration in relapse rates up to 6 months, with a plateau reached by the 12th month. This curve was considered by Hunt and his colleagues to represent the extinction that occurs when new learning begins to decay over time.

However, Litman, Eiser, and Taylor (1979) have examined this approach and conclude that this is only a cumulative survival curve, that is, it shows only how many survivors (abstainers) are left at a given point in time. Graphs based on group means obscure *individual* patterns of relapse. In addition, the assumption for the graph is that those who relapsed are still actively pursuing their addictions in later months. There is no accounting of the many relapsers who began abstinence anew. As mentioned earlier, addiction follows a highly fluctuating and idiosyncratic course, and such averaging may make treatment look less useful than it is. The individual who relapsed by having one drink in the third month and then stopped

---

**Alcoholics who are easily located presumably live in more stable situations and are therefore less likely to drink. In addition, requiring replies by mail may have inadvertently selected out more motivated individuals than if direct telephone contact was made.

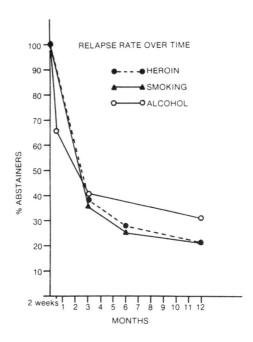

FIGURE 1.1.   Relapse patterns for heroin addicts, smokers, and alcoholics. **Note:** From W.
A. Hunt, L. W. Barnett, and L. G. Branch (1971), "Relapse rates in addiction programs." *Journal
of Clinical Psychology, 27,* 455–456. Reprinted with permission of Clinical Psychology Publishing
Co., Inc., 4 Conant Square, Brandon, VT 05733.

drinking is treated the same statistically as the individual who began
drinking at the same time and continued. There is no distinction between
lapsing and relapsing.

Why is this issue important? Because treatment outcome studies lose
sight of the "natural history" (Vaillant, 1983) and "career" (Maddux &
Desmond, 1986) aspects of addiction. Each patient needs to be evaluated
in terms of his own idiosyncratic patterns. Applying the same explanations
to all addicts and alcoholics will ultimately cloud one's understanding. As
Schachter (1982) states,

> They [research studies] correctly describe the results of a single attempt to
> quit smoking or lose weight or what have you, but from such results nothing
> can or should be inferred about the probable success of a lifetime of effort
> to quit smoking or lose weight . . . Because literally hundreds of studies
> . . . have repeatedly reported pathetic rates of success, we have concluded
> that the addictive behaviors are unyielding, almost hopeless disorders. (pp.
> 443)

For example, telling a recovering person that one encounter with alcohol
or drugs will result in an immediate loss of control is inaccurate and

potentially harmful. Many relapsers have experienced periods of controlled or minimal use that resulted in full-blown relapses when loss of control is what they expected. Explaining to people that there are many ways in and out of substance use is more realistic.

Spontaneous Remission

Do all alcoholics and addicts need treatment? Research suggests that there are large numbers of people who are able to stop drug use on their own (Prugh, 1986). Smart (1976) estimates the annual spontaneous remission rate of alcoholics to be between 1% and 33%. Miller and Hester (1987) report an average 1-year "abstinent and improved" spontaneous remission rate of 19% in alcoholics.

Many young drinkers "age out" of their alcohol abuse. Cahalan and Room (1974) found that greater drinking problems occurred in younger age groups than in older age groups. Twenty-five percent of males 21 to 29 years old, 13% of males 50 to 59 years old, and 1% of males 70 and older reported such problems. Kandel and Raveis (1989) report that illicit drug use peaks in the teens and that many adolescents quit marijuana and cocaine use decisively by their late 20s. Substance use is often replaced with increased concerns about family, occupational, health, and financial issues.

Studies of obese and nicotine-addicted populations also show much spontaneous remission. Schachter (1982) reported that many untreated individuals are able to lose a larger amount of weight and stop smoking for a longer period than those receiving formal intervention. Approximately 95% of the 40 million people who have quit smoking have done it on their own (Peele, 1990). This does not mean that self-changers do not relapse. Prochaska and DiClemente (1986) found that smokers generally relapse three times before they finally maintain a stable abstinence.

For any treatment to be considered successful it should produce higher success rates than would be expected by spontaneous remission. At this point, however, it is unclear whether spontaneous remitters experience less severe substance abuse than those in treatment and therefore do not need to seek help. A recent study found that 47.5% of untreated smokers were successful in quitting, while 23.6% of treated smokers were successful. The more severe smokers tended to use cessation programs (Fiore et al., 1990).

A final consideration is that the quality of untreated recoveries relative to treated recoveries has not been determined empirically. Many disease-oriented professionals suggest that untreated people will inevitably progress to a state of deterioration (Johnson, 1985; Milam & Ketcham, 1981). However, there are indications (among alcoholics and cocaine addicts) that successful untreated and treated people adopt similar tactics in stopping their substance use, such as changing daily routines, developing spirituality, building social support, and avoiding alcohol and drug cues (Shaffer & Jones, 1989; Vaillant, 1983).

RELAPSE STATISTICS

A thorough review of treatment outcome is beyond the scope of this book. However, I would like to review outcome briefly from three different viewpoints: (a) short- and long-term outcome of treated substance abusers, (b) comparative treatment settings, and (c) spontaneous recovery (outcome of untreated individuals). The great majority of these studies deal with alcoholism, but research suggests that relapse rates across addictions are quite similar (Brownell, Marlatt, Lichtenstein, & Wilson, 1986; Hunt, Barnett, & Branch, 1971).

Lapses are so common among all addictions that most studies include an "improved" category to accommodate them. Definitions of this state vary widely (depending on the theoretical stance of the researcher), but most often they include a significant decrease in drinking episodes; improved quality of social, legal, occupational, health, or family functioning; or a period of abstinence (such as 1 month) prior to the follow-up period.

Overall Treatment Outcome

Curiosity about treatment outcome is nothing new. Eduard Levinstein, a 19th-century physician in Berlin, was rather pessimistic about the cure of morphine addiction (cited in Musto, 1987). Dr. Levinstein wrote a book entitled *Morbid Craving for Morphia* and reported a relapse rate of 75% in those weaned from opiates. Despite methodological issues, such as a limited follow-up, this figure holds up well today.

The average 1-year success rate of alcoholism treatment programs is about 30% (Hunt, Barnett, & Branch, 1971). Miller and Hester (1980) report similar results (26%). When success is viewed as total abstinence, the figures are quite disappointing. Baekland, Lundwall, and Kissin (1975) reviewed 30 inpatient treatment studies and found improvement (less than total abstinence) rates of 50%. However, when corrected for spontaneous remission and attrition, these rates drop to about 30%. Costello (1975a) grouped 58 studies from best to poorest, finding a range of successful abstainers from 12% to 45%. The percentage of alcoholics was between 44% and 60%. In an update of this review, he concluded that over a relatively long period of time improvement occurs in about 45% of patients receiving good treatment (Costello, 1975b). A similar percentage experience more serious relapses.

Miller and Hester (1987) sum up these results as follows: (a) at 6 months, 32% will be abstinent and 34% will be improved; (b) at 1 year, 26% will be abstinent or improved; and (c) the steep relapse curve characteristic of early posttreatment flattens out with the passage of time.

Longer term follow-up studies further indicate the high recurrence of drinking. The controversial Rand Report (Armor, Polich, & Stambul, 1978) showed that a large percentage of alcoholics go into remission for periods of time, but many relapse and seek treatment again. Only 7% of the total sample of about 2,000 patients remained completely abstinent for 4 years. Helzer and his associates (1985) followed 1,289 alcoholics for 5 to 7 years after treatment. At the end of this time only 15% never touched alcohol while 79% were drinking heavily.

Similar relapse rates are found with other drug addictions. About 50% of methadone maintenance graduates (Stimmel & Rabin, 1974) and about 66% of outpatient methadone detoxified patients (Maddux, Desmond, & Esquivel, 1980) relapse. A relapse range of 50% to 90% has been found for opiate addicts discharged from a public service hospital (Stephens & Cottrell, 1972). Hunt et al. (1971) found an abstinence rate of 20% in heroin addicts at 1-year follow-up. In a nationwide study of publicly funded addiction treatment programs, Hubbard, Marsden, Rachal, Harwood, Cavanaugh, and Ginzburg (1989) reported that heroin and cocaine addicts treated for at least 3 months decreased their usage by three-quarters and one-half, respectively. If they received residential treatment for more than 1 year, their usage dropped even further. The latter group was much more likely to be employed and to avoid criminal acts.

Do demographic variables make a difference? Apparently they do. Baekland (1977) found that "good prognosis" patients (higher socioeconomic status and social stability) had success rates between 32% and 68%, while "poor prognosis" (skid row) patients had rates between 0% and 18%.

This finding has been borne out by recent studies at two private treatment centers. One study found a combined (alcohol and drugs) abstinence rate of 46% among discharged patients ("Evaluation Consortium," 1989). Eleven percent did not respond to the follow-up questionnaire. Patients who were older, married, and had some postsecondary education showed better results. The other study, which focused on "socially stable" alcoholics, found a 66% continuous abstention rate at 6 months (Wallace, McNeill, Gilfillan, MacLean, & Fanella, 1988).

Adolescent substance abuse has been proliferating at a rapid rate. Two recent studies have found relapse rates similar to those adults. Brown, Vik, and Creamer (1989) followed adolescent substance abusers for 3 and 6 months after treatment and found that about two-thirds relapsed within the first 3 months. About 70% relapsed by the sixth month. Wallace (1989) reports that 76% of adolescent cocaine users in her study relapsed within the first 3 months.

Taken together, these studies can be interpreted as suggesting that current treatment fails. On the other hand, they also suggest that a large pool of improved patients exists. I support the more optimistic interpretation: Treatment can be considered a failure only if perfection (i.e., total and continuous abstinence) is the goal. This does not mean that we have to abandon abstinence-oriented treatment, but we should provide such treatment more realistically. The goal in *all* medical treatments is to eliminate *all* symptoms, but patients receiving other forms of treatment need not regard them as failures if symptoms recur. Other medical treatments usually set criteria for improvement. The same should be true for addictions.

Comparison of Treatment Settings

Although treatment has beneficial effects for many people, there is little evidence that the setting makes a difference. Specific findings have been addressed in greater detail elsewhere, but a brief review will underscore the major points.

Despite claims in the treatment industry that inpatient treatment is more successful than outpatient treatment, outcome studies provide less dramatic findings. Baekland (1977) found higher rates of improvement in outpatient clinics than in inpatient programs, but the outpatient clinics had higher dropout rates (37% vs. 17%). Miller and Hester (1986) later reviewed 26 controlled studies and found consistent results: No studies showed superior improvements using residential care. In fact, differences that were observed favored nonresidential (outpatient and partial hospitalization) settings.

The effect of socioeconomic variables is important in outcome in these different settings. Miller and Hester (1986) concluded that severely addicted, socially unstable alcoholics fare better in inpatient settings, while less severely addicted, socially stable alcoholics perform better in outpatient settings. Mixing these populations results in comparable or better results in outpatient treatments.

These findings support those of Costello (1977), that good outcomes are associated with such interventions as involvement of employers, family therapy, and social casework. Antabuse, behavioral therapy, and screening procedures that eliminate high-risk individuals also enhance outcome. However, even an effective inpatient program can be rendered useless if an intensive community milieu and aggressive outpatient follow-up are not utilized. Ahles, Schlundt, Prue, and Rychtarik (1983) found that behavioral aftercare contracts and calendar prompts improved patients' levels of functioning. Discontinuation of the aftercare contract resulted in significantly lower abstinence rates.

Comparison of Treatment Modalities

Miller and Hester (1986) reviewed the major treatment methods in the alcoholism field and discovered that the most frequently used methods lack empirical support. Popular approaches such as confrontation, traditional psychotherapy, alcoholism education, group therapy, and administration of Antabuse receive little support in outcome literature. There is little research supporting the effectiveness of Alcoholics Anonymous, but the structure and philosophy of this self-help organization do not allow controlled research to take place. Approaches such as aversion therapy, marital or family therapy, social skills training, and stress management have received empirical support in the literature. Self-control training may be effective for problem drinkers without significant levels of dependence, but is not effective for chronic alcoholics who are severely alcohol dependent.

RELAPSE ACROSS THE
ADDICTIONS

Nicotine Addiction

Despite its notable absence from the "drug war," nicotine use produces a powerful addiction. Henningfield (1984) reports, "To the extent that experimentation leads to ultimate chronic use, tobacco appears to have an 'addictive potential' similar to that of opium" (p. 25). Professionals in the addiction field often encounter heroin addicts who regard nicotine addiction as their greatest therapeutic challenge.

These perceptions are borne out by research. Following treatment for smoking, 70% to 80% of smokers relapse within 1 year (Hunt & Bespalac, 1974). Approximately 25% to 30% of treated smokers are abstinent from 2 to 6 years after discharge from treatment (Colletti, Supnick, & Rizzo, 1982). Brandon, Tiffany, and Baker (1986) found that 91% return to regular smoking *after tasting one cigarette.* Perkins (1988) found that only one-third of postmyocardial infarction patients (who probably have the best reasons to stop) remain abstinent at 1 year.

Eating Disorders

Relapse studies have been conducted primarily with obese and bulimic patients. Relapse with obese populations is difficult to define, as abstinence is not an option. Sternberg (1985) defines relapse as the loss of weight followed by regaining a certain amount of this weight. Some have defined relapse as regaining 20% (Wing & Jeffery, 1978) or 50% (Gormally, Rardin,

& Black, 1980), of weight lost, while others have used absolute amounts of weight as the criteria (Leon & Chamberlain, 1973).

Regardless of success criteria, relapses among obese individuals appear to be universal. Albert Stunkard (1958) stated, "of those who do remain in treatment, most will not lose significant poundage, and of those who do lose weight, most will regain it promptly" (p. 87). In one study, 100% of dieters had at least one slip, while two-thirds gained at least five pounds within the first 60 days after treatment (Rosenthal & Marx, 1981). Increasing the length of treatment leads to greater weight loss and increased maintenance (Brownell & Wadden, 1986). Overall, at least two-thirds of those who lose weight gain it all back within a few years, while only 2% are still maintaining their original goals after 7 years (Milkman & Sunderwirth, 1987). Despite their popularity, very low calorie diets offer no advantages, as patients regain two-thirds of their lost weight within a year (Brownell, 1989).

Defining relapse in bulimia is also difficult. Bemis (1985) proposes that a bulimic can relapse by (a) returning to a binge and purge pattern, starvation and overeating, or overall dysfunctional eating, or (b) returning to foods that precipitate a binge response. Relapse could also mean returning to abuse of laxatives, diet pills, or diuretics. Whatever definition of relapse is used, behavioral and cognitive-behavioral techniques appear to effect a significant decrease in behaviors such as binge-eating, vomiting, and laxative abuse (Mitchell, Hoberman, & Pyle, 1989). However, the percentage of patients who avoid relapsing is very low. At follow-ups ranging between 6 weeks and 2 years, the majority of bulimic patients are actively bulimic (Mitchell et al., 1989).

Compulsive Gambling

The trend toward expansion of off-track betting, sports betting, and state lotteries is increasing public perception that compulsive gambling may become a national problem (Lesieur, 1986). Estimates of the numbers of compulsive gamblers in the United States range from 1 to 9 million individuals (Knapp & Lech, 1987). Many compulsive gamblers are also involved in alcohol or drug abuse (Lesieur, Blume, & Zoppa, 1986).

The literature contains numerous case studies and uncontrolled research reports concerning treatment of compulsive gamblers. One study of an inpatient treatment program found that of 60 patients responding to a questionnaire at 1-year follow-up, 55% were abstinent and 21.5% reported some gambling with current abstinence (Russo, Taber, McCormick, & Ramirez, 1984). However, in the absence of controlled research, further conclusions are not possible.

SUMMARY

The studies reviewed here suggest that the goal of total abstinence is difficult for most alcoholics and addicts to reach after only one treatment. Applying treatment in an inpatient setting does not appear to improve outcome consistently. Moreover, relapse rates and patterns with alcoholism and drug abuse are similar to those for nicotine addiction, eating disorders, and compulsive gambling. On the basis of these findings, the following formulation of relapse is used throughout this book:

> **Relapse** is the reinstatement of addictive behavior, thoughts, and feelings after a period of abstinence. This period of abstinence can be highly variable, but should consist of more than a withdrawal period. Relapse involves an interaction of biological, psychological, and social factors. The precise contribution of each of these factors for a particular individual will depend upon his or her learning history, physical functioning, psychological predispositions, and environment. Relapse should not necessarily be considered an indication of one's motivation, but should be regarded as a *mistake* that can be corrected through examination and remediation of individual risk factors. A brief return to addictive behavior should *not* be considered a relapse unless it occurs frequently or triggers a protracted return to an addictive behavior pattern. Such lapses may actually provide clues about biological, psychological, or social factors that require further assessment. Finally, the replacement of one addictive behavior with another should be considered a potential sign of lapse or relapse.

Despite the consistency of relapse among addictions, there are many misconceptions about the meaning of relapse. The next chapter addresses the mythology surrounding this phenomenon.

Chapter 2
Relapse Mythology

In New York drunks were confined in the
Asylum for Inebriates on Blackwell's
Island. Released after a few days of
abstinence, they often went on a new
binge, and incarcerated again, became
known as "rounders."
— Otto Bettman (1974)

One of the more enduring myths in modern society is that alcoholism
and drug addiction are contemporary problems that our forebears did not
experience. As Bettman (1974) states,

> That essentially American problem, drug addiction, has a longer history than
> most of us may suspect. Opium use, which had become a national habit as
> early as 1840, found its devotees in all classes and religions. . . . The drug
> addiction of today—a most painful reflection of American society—had its
> origin in the good old days. (p. 133)

Musto (1987), speaking of cocaine, wrote, "At first, in the 1880s, it had
been welcomed as an ideal tonic, but after a decade or so its image had
become more questionable, and by 1900 it was considered to be the most
dangerous of all drugs" (p. x).

The process of relearning what our ancestors experienced is nowhere
more evident than in relapse prevention. There are numerous relapse
myths about alcoholism, drug use, and other addictions that ultimately
negate our efforts. As on Blackwell's Island, we approach treatment with
a "revolving door" mentality and hope that we will not create "rounders."
However, as is clear from chapter 1, the ability to maintain abstinence
(however defined) is more elusive than stopping the addiction.

This chapter will examine many of the myths related to addiction and

14

relapse. Some are drawn from observations made in literature on relapse (Gorski & Miller, 1986; Schiffman, Read, Maltese, Rapkin, & Jarvik, 1985; Washton, 1989), but others are drawn from my personal discussions with patients and professionals.

FIFTEEN MYTHS OF RELAPSE

Relapse Is an Unpredictable Occurrence

Relapse is often quite predictable. The studies mentioned earlier make it clear that relapse is experienced by the great majority of people attempting to eliminate their addictions. Even those who obtain treatment are likely to relapse at some point. With or without treatment, those who develop stable and reliable strategies toward abstinence experience a much lower likelihood of relapse. Those who maintain high risk behaviors and unstructured lifestyles will often view relapse as unpredictable.

In my interviews with relapsed addicts and alcoholics, I have often heard them say, "I just found myself with a drink in my hand" or "I was doing really well and then one day I ended up using drugs." When I question them further, I usually find these perceptions to be erroneous. Relapsers often engage in high risk activities such as frequenting bars, going to parties where drugs are present, and keeping drug paraphernalia. They may have difficulty managing emotions such as depression and anger. Their environments may be disruptive. Many live in neighborhoods where access to drugs and alcohol is easy. Social conflict and psychosocial stressors are known to increase relapse risk. Lack of involvement in self-help or treatment activities can also interfere with recovery.

This myth is insidious because it can lead people to believe they are passive and helpless. Should relapse occur, they regard it as a random event instead of looking for causal patterns (which are usually present). Professionals in the field often mirror their patients' reaction because their own misconceptions about relapse leave them feeling inadequate. They become part of the problem by simply repeating earlier strategies or waiting for the patient to become "ready" for treatment.

Relapse Begins with the First Episode of Substance Use

Many recovering persons believe that abstinence is the only goal of recovery. As long as they remain drug free, they feel that they are making progress. Unfortunately, this approach confuses the end with the means. Abstinence, participation in A.A., treatment, or any other approach one cares to choose simply provides a way to improve the quality of life. As people proceed through recovery, they often develop improved communication skills, better relationships, and self-efficacy. These tools enhance a sense of belonging and meaning that prevents life from being perceived as burdensome and unsatisfying. In the absence of such coping mechanisms, addictive behavior may be regarded as the only option.

Another distinction is important here. A *lapse* can be considered a short-lived return to substance use that is followed by a reflection upon one's mistakes. *Relapse* would result from a lack of learning and a repetition of the pattern that led to the lapse.

Relapse Results from a Lack of Willpower

Willpower is a hallmark of the "moral weakness" explanation of addiction. This approach regards those who become addicted as morally or constitutionally weak. The solution is to become a more moral person by attaining religious beliefs or learning discipline. A "60 Minutes" segment aired in early 1990 showed drug addicts in Singapore engaging in strenuous physical training in a prison-like setting. Authorities in Singapore believe that such regimentation will improve the addicts' self-discipline. William Bennett, the first U.S. "drug czar," has suggested a similar approach as part of the war on drugs.

The willpower approach focuses on mind over matter but in a simplistic way. It does not focus on avoiding difficult situations but on confronting them. Willpower is necessary only when a person is in a high risk situation. Obviously, there are times when such situations cannot be avoided, but those who need to rely on willpower repeatedly are probably taking unnecessary risks.

People Decide Consciously That They Want to Relapse

Addiction creates much automatic behavior. Alcoholics and addicts develop a set of behaviors that become second nature. These may include the rituals involved in using drugs, a daily routine that is built around substance use, or objects associated with substance use. Exposure to these situations may act as triggers for relapse. In responding to relapse triggers, relapsers often begin performing these behaviors in a reflexive manner.

As a result, relapsers make *unconscious* decisions that bring them closer to their drug of choice. Most relapsers are not aware of the triggers that set these behaviors into action and after relapsing may view the relapse as a random event. Others, however, may treat these individuals as if they planned a return to substance use. Because of this attitude there may be a tendency among abusers to hide the relapse for fear that others will interpret it as a devious act.

Relapse Occurs Only When the Original Drug of Choice Is Used

One of the most deceptive and common myths of relapse is that it occurs only with use of the originally abused drug. Many people in early recovery act as if there were separate recoveries for each drug that they take. Some even calculate "sobriety dates" independently for each drug. I once treated a woman who reported that she had been sober (from alcohol) for 7 years, but she had been abusing prescription medication during this period.

An even more frequent example of this myth involves alcoholics who use (but do not abuse) marijuana. Counselors who attempt to convince these alcoholics that they should attempt to cease *all* drug use are met with such responses as "What's wrong with a joint now and then?" Such logic allows a continued reliance upon chemical problem-solving solutions and high-risk situations. Substitution of alternative drugs is well known among drug users and serves only to perpetuate the cycle of relapse.

Substitution is not limited to substance use; it can include other compulsive behaviors. Compulsive gambling, eating, working, and even spending have been noted in alcoholics and drug addicts prior to relapse. These behaviors often represent an escape from direct communication and development of self-knowledge.

Relapsers Enter Recovery Only When They "Hit Bottom"

The "hitting bottom" concept is a central theme in A.A. It assumes that pain has a linear relationship with success: the more pain, the better. However, many alcoholics and addicts are in a high degree of pain at the outset and some use substances to medicate this pain. An increase in pain often immobilizes them to the point of hopelessness.

As Figure 2.1 indicates, the optimal level of motivation is usually found at a moderate level of arousal (Hebb, 1955). Increasing the arousal (pain) past the optimal point creates a more intense, and less motivating, level of arousal. This observation has implications for interventions such as confrontation, which tend to create resistance in patients already in a high state of pain. Such treatment is much more suitable for "low pain" patients as it can potentially increase pain to an optimal level—a possible explanation for the mixed results obtained with confrontation (Miller, 1985).

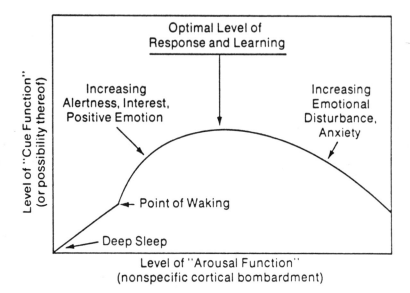

FIGURE 2.1.   Hebb's optimal level of response and learning curve. From D. Hebb (1955), "Drives and the C.N.S." *Psychological Review, 62,* 243–253.

Relapse Means Failure

The myth that relapse means failure is tied to the notion that an attempt at recovery can be measured at a single point in time. Rather than focusing on the recovering individual's balance of strengths and weaknesses, attention is paid only to the actual substance usage. This focus prevents a mobilization of strengths when they are needed most. Instead, relapse should be regarded as a mistake that has arisen due to a lack of knowledge or skills. The relapser has probably engaged in high-risk activities or built an incomplete recovery plan. Reviewing these mistakes provides a positive framework for change rather than a negative and judgmental atmosphere. When a relapse is treated this way, if there is another in the future, the recovering alcoholic or addict will be much more likely to discuss it openly.

Relapse Negates Any Growth Made up to That Point

Because of the focus on abstinence, there is a misconception that one needs to "start from square one" after a relapse. Those who have been counting their days of sobriety in A.A. must begin their count again. However, it is not as if the alcoholic or addict has forgotten all previous knowledge when a relapse occurs. Most relapsers retain much learned information that they can use in the future. Recovery is a stepwise learning process in which there may be downward steps, but which, one hopes, leads to an overall upward trend.

The myth that a relapse negates all growth is dangerous because relapsers can easily become discouraged. They may assume that they have to repeat their earlier learning, a step which could increase their guilt and embarrassment. Anyone who has worked with relapsers knows that shame and embarrassment can lead to avoidance and extend the relapse episode. These feelings are especially acute among long-term abstainers who then relapse. Such individuals do not have to relearn old material; they need to focus on unattended areas in their recoveries. Stepwise learning through correction of mistakes can bring relapsers back into recovery much sooner.

Relapse Means That the Relapser Is Not Motivated

When there is a negative outcome to treatment, often the explanation is that the relapser is not motivated. While there are certainly many alcoholics and addicts who make insufficient efforts toward recovery, clinicians need to be careful not to confuse motivation with compliance. The patient may truly want to stop abusing drugs or alcohol but may have difficulty complying because of cognitive deficits, inadequate social support, or past negative treatment experiences. If clinicians assist the patient in breaking these barriers rather than expecting a ready-made package of motivation when the patient enters treatment, then outcome can certainly be enhanced.

In addition, the patient may lack knowledge of important high-risk factors that he or she needs to address. Educational efforts can help the patient develop the understanding necessary for a positive outcome. Most important, the clinician needs to assess the roots of insufficient motivation instead of relegating the patient to the "unmotivated" category.

All Recovering Individuals Have the Same Relapse Potential

One of the advantages of the traditional disease model is that it assumes an ever-present danger of relapse. While this notion may keep recovering people vigilant, one should not assume that everyone has the same level of risk. Risk is dependent on a variety of biological, psychological, and social factors that differ among recovering individuals. Risk is a function of behavior; to suggest that there is no way to control it is erroneous.

Assumption of a passive stance can only reduce vigilance to warning signs and precipitate a relapse.

Relapse Involves Use of Alcohol and Drugs Only

The belief that relapse involves only alcohol and drug use is an open invitation to replace substance abuse with compulsive behaviors such as eating disorders (particularly bulimia), "workaholism," compulsive gambling and spending, excessive reliance on sex and relationships, and caffeine and nicotine abuse.

Because primary attention is paid to substance use, many recovering individuals assume that such replacements are acceptable. However, the consequences of these addictions can be as deleterious as the original addictions. One recovering heroin addict remained abstinent for 36 months but began abusing his credit cards during that time. He ran up a bill of $29,000 and eventually relapsed. One recovering alcoholic worked 100-hour weeks until he became extremely fatigued and turned to alcohol. In both cases, their peers thought that these individuals were adapting well to recovery and had no significant problems.

Withdrawal Is Complete Within Several Days

Although the acute effects of drugs and alcohol last for a relatively short period of time, neuropsychological research strongly indicates that there are longer lasting cognitive dysfunctions that can extend for months or even years (Gorski & Miller, 1986; Parsons, 1987). This phenomenon is usually referred to as *postacute withdrawal* (Gorski & Miller, 1986) or *protracted withdrawal syndrome* (Kissin, 1979). Difficulties such as memory disturbance, problems with abstract reasoning, sleep interruption, emotional imbalance, and sensitivity to stress are often present.

Although the phenomenology of this syndrome is highly variable, it is important to recognize the confusion caused by its symptoms in early recovery. Many people in early recovery mistakenly assume that their clarity of thinking will return to normal shortly after withdrawal and become upset when these symptoms are still present months later. They regard the symptoms as representative of recovery rather than as consequences of addiction. Some become frustrated and return to alcohol or drugs. As a result, it is critical that those in early recovery be informed of cognitive changes that may occur.

Relapsers Should Receive the Same Treatment as Other Substance Abusers

For many years, the typical response to relapse was to recycle the relapser through the same treatment that he or she received prior to the relapse. Treatment professionals assumed that the relapser was not motivated or had not "hit bottom," so a repetition of treatment would provide the appropriate refresher. They thought that reminders to attend A.A., seek sponsorship, and "ask for help" would suffice. Ironically, there tended to be little discussion of the circumstances surrounding the relapse and even less formal assessment. As a result, alcoholics did not gain any insight into important cognitive and behavioral tendencies and often drifted back into further relapses.

Professionals now recognize that ignorance of such vital information is counterproductive; they realize that relapses can be viewed as mistakes that provide clues about the weaknesses in a person's recovery. Correction of these weaknesses constitutes the stepwise learning needed for long-term recovery.

Relapse Is Caused by Negative Events in a Person's Life

While it is wrong to consider relapse a random event, it is equally misguided to consider that it is caused by particular negative events. It is not the actual event but the *perception* of the event that is crucial. Blaming relapse on situations can often enhance denial, as many alcoholics and addicts make excuses for their behavior. I was once told by a relapser that he broke his sobriety when he became angry that his garage opener did not work. Another person relapsed when he became angry at a slow-moving "express" line at the grocery store. On the other hand, I have heard of people who maintain their recoveries in the face of serious emotional traumas such as family deaths, accidents, and personal misfortune. There is not enough attention paid to those who are resilient in dealing with such stress.

In addition, many alcoholics and addicts report relapse after *positive* developments such as promotions at work, commendation from friends and relatives, or financial success. Some individuals become complacent and drift away from methods that assisted them in developing sobriety in the first place. Members of A.A. refer to this phenomenon as a "pink cloud." To avoid this pitfall it is important for the recovering person not to overestimate his or her progress.

Treatment Professionals Have No Ability to Predict Relapse

The myth that relapses cannot be predicted by clinicians encourages a pessimistic attitude toward treatment for professional and patient alike. As stated earlier, the belief that relapse is random can be quite counterproductive in recovery. In fact, patients provide many clues about their relapse potential while in treatment. In addition, much is known about biological, psychological, and social factors that lead to relapse. These factors appear to operate at some level in all addictions. A comprehensive and systematic approach to assessment will provide a good estimate of relapse potential.

SUMMARY

This chapter examined myths about relapse that can impede treatment. These myths revolve around explanations for relapse such as willpower, motivation, and unpredictability. Relapse is better explained as an incomplete assessment of relapse factors. The following chapter provides an examination of various models of relapse and what they contribute to an understanding of these factors.

Chapter 3

Models of Relapse

> *Do not quench your inspiration and your*
> *imagination; do not become the slave of*
> *your model.*
> > *— Vincent van Gogh*

Depending on one's viewpoint, the route to recovery can be accomplished in a variety of ways. One's beliefs about how people begin addictive behavior will probably affect beliefs about how people stop addictive behavior. Although there has been little discussion about how different models of addiction are applied to relapse, each model has at least implicit assumptions as to how relapsers should be treated. Unfortunately, while some of these models are counterproductive to relapse prevention they are still actively used in the substance abuse field.

This chapter describes three of the major models of addiction (the moral, disease, and self-medication models) and delineates the ways in which each may *interfere* with prevention of relapse. Over the past 15 years, clinicians and researchers have developed relapse prevention models in response to these difficulties. Three such models have been utilized: (a) cognitive-behavioral (Annis, 1986; Marlatt & Gordon, 1985; Monti, Abrams, Kadden, & Cooney, 1989); (b) recovery training (Zackon, McAuliffe, & Ch'ien, 1985); and (c) relapse prevention planning (Gorski & Miller, 1986). The fourth to be discussed is the biopsychosocial model, which integrates empirically derived factors into a comprehensive approach to assessment and treatment.

MORAL MODEL

The moral model can be viewed from religious and legal perspectives. The religious perspective regards substance use as caused by sin and a lack of spiritual understanding (as opposed to a temperance model, which blames alcoholism on alcohol). Those who violate religious doctrines are deemed "sinners" and considered "bad." Drunkenness is an unnatural state that potentially threatens traditional family and social structure; as a result, abstinence is the goal. Drinking is thought to release undesirable aggressive and sexual impulses, so those who knowingly drink are inviting trouble. This is evident in sayings such as "When you walk into a bar, the devil walks in behind you." In order to correct this aberration, alcoholics need to admit their sins and follow spiritual guidelines. The clergy are the appropriate intervention agents.

From a legal standpoint, the drinker is voluntarily violating social rules and norms. Rather than ascribing causality to a lack of spirituality, the violation is considered a "crime" and punishment is meted out. The criminal then pays his debt to society. Drinking may also be considered a violation of social norms, and the drinker may be seen as lazy or otherwise undesirable. In order to stop drinking, individuals are encouraged to make personal moral decisions and to use willpower. Legal and social authorities are the appropriate intervention agents.

Because the drinker is viewed as morally culpable, relapse is viewed as a regression in moral judgment. A relapser is seen as giving in to weakness and lacking in sincerity. When applied to relapse, the moral perspective can be extremely counterproductive as it induces guilt and shame. Marlatt's (1985a) term *abstinence violation effect* refers to the guilt that one experiences after a relapse. This guilt can precipitate a full-blown relapse. Rather than induce guilt, the goal should be to encourage the relapser to take responsibility for correcting his or her mistakes. When guilt is a desired effect, there will be a greater tendency on the part of the substance user to hide relapses and to use substances to mediate the negative feelings.

DISEASE MODEL

The medical disease model has many advantages over the moral viewpoint as it removes the moral stigma and opens up the possibility of treatment. Instead of moral weakness, biological, genetic, and innate characterological predispositions are thought to cause addiction. Those who are labeled *alcoholic* or *addict* are considered qualitatively different from moderate users. In this view, alcoholism and drug addiction are progressive, irreversible diseases that ultimately result in death if left untreated. Any usage is believed to result in loss of control. Abstinence is therefore the primary goal of treatment, and the addicted person is cautioned to maintain vigilance against relapse. Recovery is considered never ending; hence, terms such as *recovering alcoholic* are favored over *recovered alcoholic*. The primary intervention agents are other recovering alcoholics and the treatment professionals.

Several implications of this model may be problematic in treating relapse. First, the belief that one has a disease may be interpreted as total absolution of responsibility should a relapse occur. Individuals may then explain relapses as an inevitable result of their disease and loss of control. This prevents a careful examination of the faulty decision-making processes that often precede relapse.

Second, the belief in loss of control may result in a self-fulfilling prophecy. Instead of differentiating between lapses and relapses, relapsers may presume that further substance usage is inevitable. Some may use the loss of control concept as an excuse to continue using substances.

Third, the disease model focuses primarily on biological factors although the preponderance of relapse precipitants are psychological and social (Marlatt & Rohsenow, 1980). Addicts and alcoholics often ask, "Isn't there some pill I can take?" The excessive focus on physical solutions takes needed attention away from lifestyle changes that promote long-term recovery from *any* addiction. It also underestimates coexisting mental disorders.

Finally, the disease approach implies that there is a provider and a patient in an inherently unequal relationship. This model places the patient in a passive position, waiting for the expected treatment. Treatment compliance research from a variety of medical disciplines indicates that patients adhere to treatment more strongly if they are actively involved as participants (Meichenbaum & Turk, 1987). Collaboration avoids the contention that confrontation is the primary treatment for relapse.

SELF-MEDICATION MODEL

Khantzian (1985) suggested that drug-dependent individuals are predisposed to addiction because they suffer from painful affective states and psychiatric disorders related to them. Rather than choosing drugs randomly, addicts are thought to select drugs that neutralize unpleasant feelings. For instance, heroin addicts use opiates because they mute rage and aggressive feelings. Cocaine addicts use cocaine to relieve distress caused by hyperactivity, depression, and hypomania. As drug use is a function of an underlying mental disorder, the goal of treatment is improved mental functioning. Psychotherapy and/or pharmacotherapy would be the treatment(s) of choice. This approach acknowledges the importance of dual diagnoses.

Unfortunately, this approach implies that the treatment of the mental disorder is sufficient. This may place the therapist in a chicken-and-egg dilemma, because it is often difficult to assess whether psychopathology preceded, coexisted with, or followed substance abuse. As is shown later in this book, many apparent mental disorders are actually secondary to addiction. Many therapists and patients who dwell on mental disturbance without establishing a foundation of abstinence find that treatment is ultimately unsuccessful. Many alcoholics and addicts use psychiatric symptoms as an excuse for substance use: "Of course I drink. Wouldn't you if you were this depressed?"

RELAPSE PREVENTION MODELS

Cognitive Behavioral Model

Alan Marlatt and his colleagues have developed an influential and comprehensive model of relapse (Donovan & Marlatt, 1988; Marlatt, 1985b; Marlatt & Gordon, 1985) that views addictive behavior as an acquired habit pattern, which can be modified or eliminated by applying the laws of learning theory. Addictions develop from a combination of classical conditioning (e.g., morning drinking to combat withdrawal) and operant conditioning (e.g., improved social functioning when drinking). Recovery is therefore seen as a learning task for which the alcoholic or addict takes responsibility. The person is considered capable of self-control. There is also a deemphasis on the *alcoholic* and *addict* labels.

The process of changing occurs in three steps. The first step involves a commitment to change. Rather than making an impulsive decision, long-term *maintainers* exhibit a readiness for and understanding of the implications of change. The second step is to implement the change. This may involve treatment or self-change. Marlatt considers this stage to be over-emphasized because many individuals do not appreciate the need for vigilance after initial change efforts. The third step is maintenance, in which relapse prevention skills are of paramount importance. This step is not only the longest and most challenging but also involves the most trials and errors. In this stage, recovery involves incremental learning and refinement of coping skills.

Marlatt and Gordon pay special attention to cognitive-behavioral factors in relapse. In disease-oriented approaches, the theory is that craving is a primary precursor to relapse, but Marlatt has evaluated a number of high-risk situations that encompass emotional, social, and psychological factors. Negative and positive emotional states, social pressure, testing of personal control, and interpersonal conflict were all found to be related to relapse. The route into these situations usually entails "apparently irrelevant decisions" (e.g., stopping at a bar ostensibly to visit friends).

There are several cognitive factors that mediate a person's ability to cope with these risks. The first factor is Bandura's (1977) concept of self-efficacy, which is the person's perception that he can cope with a prospective high-risk situation. The strength of the efficacy expectation determines the nature and power of coping behavior in response to the threat. The disease model's prediction of loss of control may actually decrease self-efficacy and increase the risk of a relapse. Difficult experiences may therefore prove insurmountable.

The second factor is outcome expectancy, which refers to a person's perception of the effects of his behavior. If one has low outcome expectancies, there is a higher risk of relapse because the person does not expect to be effective. This may cause him or her to avoid potentially effective behavior or to choose less effective alternatives. These expectancies are affected by social and cultural beliefs, self-esteem, and environmental factors.

If the alcoholic or addict is confronted with a high risk situation and experiences low self-efficacy or outcome expectancy, a lapse may occur. If the person feels a high degree of guilt and self-loathing, an abstinence violation effect is said to occur. If these intensely negative feelings are not dealt with through constructive action, they may trigger a complete relapse.

Interventions are of three types: (a) cognitive remediation, (b) skill building, and (c) lifestyle modification. Cognitive remediation includes positive self-statements, enhancement of outcome expectancy and self-efficacy, and coping imagery. Skill building includes roleplaying, self-monitoring, and relapse rehearsal. Lifestyle modification includes exercise, relaxation techniques, and effective time management.

Support for components of this model come from several sources. Cummings, Gordon, and Marlatt (1980) compared alcoholics, smokers, heroin addicts, gamblers, and overeaters, and found remarkable consistency in major relapse episodes. Negative emotional states, interpersonal conflict, and social pressure accounted for about 75% of relapses. Litman, Stapleton, Oppenheim, Peleg, and Jackson (1983) found that unpleasant mood states, external events and euphoria, and lessened cognitive vigilance accounted for 55% of the variance in relapse episodes. Other researchers have found similar results with heroin addicts (Chaney, Roszell, & Cummings, 1982), cocaine addicts (Wallace, 1989), smokers (Baer & Lichtenstein, 1988; Schiffman, 1982), and overeaters (Filstead, Parrella, & Ebbitt, 1988; Grilo, Schiffman, & Wing, 1989). These results also hold up cross-culturally (Sandahl, 1984).

Some addicts and alcoholics use substances to gain a sense of mastery over their environment. They may artificially increase self-efficacy through the initially rewarding arousal effects of alcohol (Wilson, 1987). In the absence of alcohol, such individuals may experience lowered self-efficacy. Low self-efficacy has been found to predict negative outcome in drug and alcohol abusers (Burling, Reilly, Moltzen, & Ziff, 1989; Rosenberg, 1983) and smokers (Bliss, Garvey, Heinhold, & Hitchcock, 1989; Condiotte & Lichtenstein, 1981).

Marlatt's model has also been employed in treatment studies, particularly with smokers. Hall, Rugg, Tunstall, and Jones (1984) found that behavioral coping skills training improved outcome. Schiffman (1984) found that positive "self-talk" helped smokers calling a hotline. Stevens and Hollis (1989) rehearsed coping strategies for potential relapse situations with smokers and found greater abstinence compared to discussion and no-treatment control groups.

Marlatt's approach is not limited to addictive behaviors. King and Fredericksen (1984) used relapse preparation to help joggers maintain their exercise regimens. McCrady (1989) has expanded this model to couples. However, despite the popularity of this model among researchers, there is a need for more work devoted to treatment outcome.

Coping Skills Model

Monti, Abrams, Kadden, and Cooney (1989) base their coping skills model on Bandura's (1977) social learning theory. This model advocates the following as important in the development and maintenance of alcoholism: (a) exposure to role models who drink, (b) expectancies that alcohol use will result in desirable effects, (c) reinforcement of alcohol use through reduction in tension or increased positive feelings, (d) pairing of stimuli with alcohol use (conditioning), and (e) a sense of mastery in dealing with difficult situations (self-efficacy). These factors lead to a substitution of alcohol use for the development of coping skills. The combination of such skills deficits, situational demands, and genetic vulnerability are thought to undermine one's ability to cope effectively, which can lead to relapse. As in Marlatt's model, self-efficacy plays a central role. The development of interpersonal (social) and intrapersonal (negative affect) coping skills can increase one's sense of competence and thereby decrease the potential for relapse. Empirical findings related to this model are discussed in chapter 4.

Annis (1986) has developed a coping skills model that highlights self-efficacy. The model is designed to use the Inventory of Drinking Situations, developed by Annis and Davis (1989), which assesses high risk drinking situations. Administration of the inventory is followed by completion of the Situational Confidence Questionnaire, which assesses self-efficacy in these conditions. A hierarchy of the situations is established to identify the particular skills in which training is needed. Behavioral, cognitive, and affective coping skills are the primary focus. Clients are then asked to self-monitor difficult situations and are trained in the needed skills. New behaviors are practiced through use of homework assignments. As more difficult skills are mastered by progress through the hierarchy, clients record changes in their self-efficacy.

Recovery Training and Self-Help Model

Recovery Training and Self-Help (RTSH) is a group outpatient after-care treatment that was developed for opiate addicts in New England and Hong Kong (McAuliffe & Ch'ien, 1986; Zackon, McAuliffe, & Ch'ien, 1985). The program is based on operant learning, social learning, and health promotion principles. Long-term recovery from addiction is thought to require removal of drug-related stimuli or extinction of conditioned responses to these stimuli. At the same time addicts are taught rewarding alternative responses such as recreational and social activities. There is a strong focus on development of skills that can be generalized from the treatment group to the addict's natural environment. The incorporation of both professional and self-help approaches is another feature of this program.

The RTSH program has four components: (a) a weekly recovery session, (b) a weekly self-help session, (c) weekend recreational and social activities, and (d) a support system of long-term ex-addicts. The weekly groups are highly structured and cover a variety of didactic topics such as craving, dealing with family members, developing a new social life, finding a job, and coping with relationships. The 26-week treatment includes peer-led fellowship meetings, exposure to drug-free social and community activities, and interaction with recovering addicts who share their experiences through "recovery stories." New skills are practiced through written assignments and group exercises.

Zackon et al. (1985) found that 32% of aftercare group members were able to maintain abstinence or infrequent use (less than once a month), while only 18% of addicts in a no-treatment control group were similarly successful. Aftercare group members who were initially unemployed were also more successful than control group members at obtaining jobs (69% vs. 27%, respectively). These differences held up in both cultures, suggesting that the program is quite adaptable.

Washton (1987) has applied a similar model to outpatient treatment of cocaine abusers. In the initial abstinence phase, patients are seen frequently (sometimes 4 to 5 times weekly) with a goal of 30 consecutive days of abstinence. The major topics of discussion are denial and craving. In the relapse prevention and lifestyle change phase, patients enter a recovery group that addresses issues of euphoric recall (deceptively pleasant memories of cocaine use), warning signs, the desire to test control, the abstinence violation effect, and a plan for lifestyle change. Patients then progress into the consolidation phase in which patients seek greater self-acceptance and self-awareness. In a sample of 127 patients who entered this program, 65% completed the first 6 to 12 months of treatment and 75% were drug-free at 1- to 2-year follow-up.

Relapse Prevention Planning Model

Gorski (1986) defines relapse as "the process of becoming dysfunctional in recovery." This dysfunction may be based in alcohol or drug use as typically defined by the disease-oriented models. However, Gorski also refers to "sobriety-based" dysfunctions, which involve a progression of symptoms from a period of stability to psychosocial distress to emotional or physical collapse. Relapse is regarded as a natural part of the recovery process, with a need to engage the patient over a long-term follow-up.

Identification of predisposing factors and internal and external warning signs are critical to preventing relapse. Predisposing factors include a high-stress lifestyle or personality, social conflict, poor health maintenance, multiple diagnoses, and an inadequate recovery program.

Internal factors relate to a syndrome Gorski refers to as post-acute withdrawal (PAW). PAW is a neurologically based set of cognitive dysfunctions that arise over a period of months or even years after abstinence begins. It includes an inability to think clearly, memory problems, emotional overreactions or numbness, sleep disturbances, physical coordination problems, and stress sensitivity (Gorski & Miller, 1986). A lack of attention to these symptoms is thought to increase the risk of relapse.

External factors result from the emergence of family, work, social, or relationship problems. These psychosocial events aggravate internal brain dysfunctions and eventually lead to loss of control over behavior. The alcoholic or addict often resorts to self-medication to prevent emotional collapse.

Gorski and Miller (1986) apply a developmental approach to the process of recovery. They hypothesize six phases of recovery, each of which involves a different task. These phases are (a) pretreatment, in which an alcoholic attempts to control alcohol use (and fails); (b) stabilization, in which alcoholics recognize their inability to use alcohol or drugs safely; (c) early recovery, in which they establish a recovery program; (d) middle recovery, in which a balanced lifestyle is developed; (e) late recovery, in which improved quality of personal functioning is established; and (f) maintenance, in which relapse prevention skills become a part of the alcoholic's lifestyle. Through each of these phases, the alcoholic is taught to recognize warning signs and implement behavioral changes that minimize risk of relapse. Patient education, inventory training (listing of warning signs), involvement of significant others, and self-help are all encouraged.

Despite its face validity and popularity among mainstream addictions counselors, no data supporting the efficacy of this approach are available. However, its recognition of cognitive dysfunction as a precursor to relapse is a contribution to the relapse prevention literature.

BIOPSYCHOSOCIAL MODEL

All of the above-mentioned models stress biological, psychological, and social components to different degrees. The need to evaluate and treat addicted individuals from multiple perspectives is by now well established, as each individual has a unique combination of biological, psychological, and social risk factors (Donovan, 1988; Lindesmith, 1968; Zucker & Gomberg, 1986). This biopsychosocial perspective allows for several unique assumptions that transcend traditional approaches:

1. The three systems (biological, psychological, and social) are not only important individually but also in how they interact. For instance, alcohol has powerful physical effects, but these effects are mediated by a drinker's perception of these effects. Marlatt and his coworkers (Marlatt, Demming, & Reid, 1973; Marlatt & Rohsenow, 1980) have demonstrated how alcoholics, given bogus alcoholic drinks, respond as if they were drinking the "real thing" (i.e., they drank more). When given true alcoholic drinks and told that these were nonalcoholic, they drank less. This effect can be observed in real-life settings also. A recovering alcoholic bartender once told me that people who drank nonalcoholic beer in his bar often "acted drunk." We cannot assume that alcoholics and drug addicts respond (or developed their addictions) in a purely physiological way.

2. The pathways by which addictions develop in each individual are highly variable (Tarter, 1988). Some people have a high biological loading, while others are affected more by psychological and social effects. Relapses depend on the balance of these factors and how well prepared the alcoholic or addict is to cope with each. The balance of these factors may change throughout the life span (Zucker & Gomberg, 1986). For instance, peer pressure may contribute more to an adolescent's relapse while health factors may play a greater role in an elderly alcoholic's relapse.

3. Peele (1985) maintains that people do not become addicted to an object but to expectations about the experience. Traditional approaches contend that "alcoholics drink because they are alcoholics" or "alcoholics relapse because alcoholism is a disease of relapse." This circular logic does not account for the reality that some people become addicted and others do not. The object of the assessment process is not only the addictive behavior but perceptions of the addictive experience.

4. The biopsychosocial model can better explain commonalities across addictions. Some people may branch out into other addictions because they become addicted to a set of experiences that can be produced by various behaviors or substances. Those with multiple addictions would have a greater likelihood of relapse because of the higher number of "triggers" for these addictions.

5. Individualized assessment within a biopsychosocial framework can

improve treatment matching. Given the homogeneous, "vanilla only" nature of current treatment, it is not surprising that treatment outcome suffers. This perspective is similar to treating all cardiac patients with the same medication or surgery.

6. In the biopsychosocial approach, knowledge about vulnerabilities that predict the initiation of substance use is applied to relapse prevention. The factors that predict the development of addiction may also explain relapse (Wesson, Havassy, & Smith, 1986).

7. Because biopsychosocial explanations have been presented both by disease model advocates (Wallace, 1988) and by social learning advocates (Donovan, 1988), there is potential for cross-fertilization, even though the correspondence between viewpoints may not be exact. The biopsychosocial model supports not only an integration of techniques but also a theoretical synthesis among models. Beitman, Goldfried, and Norcross (1989) refer to the former as technical eclecticism and the latter as theoretical eclecticism. Integrative models may have greater potential for maximizing treatment outcome (Brower, Blow, & Beresford, 1989).

SUMMARY

This chapter reviewed the moral, disease, self-medication, and relapse prevention models of relapse. Each model focuses on an important aspect of relapse, but there is little integration of models. The biopsychosocial model was presented as a perspective that combines the useful features of the other models. In the next chapter evidence is reviewed for specific biological, psychological, and social risk factors that can be applied in assessment and treatment.

Chapter 4

Biopsychosocial Factors in Relapse

I don't know who my grandfather was; I am much more concerned to know what his grandson will be.
—Abraham Lincoln

As a result of the debate over the disease concept, much effort has been devoted to explaining the genetic and biological factors in addiction. However, this knowledge is limited in its application to treating a person who is already addicted. Because there is currently no biological cure for addiction, treatment efforts should target factors that have some potential for change. These factors are primarily psychological and social.

Current research and clinical literature stress the need for comprehensive biopsychosocial assessment. The following sections report current information about the biological, psychological, and social factors related to relapse. Most of this review is based on the large volume of research on alcoholics, but research involving drug addicts or other addicted populations is included when available. In addition, many of the data are correlational, making causative explanations hazardous. This review is not meant to be definitive but is representative of the biopsychosocial approach.

BIOPSYCHOSOCIAL RISK FACTORS

Biological Risk Factors

Biological risk factors are often considered to be the primary "triggers" for relapse. The following section reviews family history, severity of addiction, neurological and neuropsychological impairments, cue reactivity, and biochemical deficiencies as factors in relapse. As this section demonstrates, the relationship between these factors and relapse is multidimensional and seldom clear-cut.

Family History and Severity The presence of genetic vulnerability in alcoholic families has been widely cited as a major causal factor in the development of alcoholism in offspring. Results supporting the genetic vulnerability viewpoint come from twin (Hrubec & Omenn, 1981), adoption (Bohman, Sigvardsson, & Cloninger, 1981; Goodwin et al., 1974), and half-sibling (Schuckit, Goodwin, & Winokur, 1972) studies. Genetic research with drug abusers is relatively rare, so any suggestions of a genetic link remain inconclusive (Pickens & Svikis, 1988).

Goodwin (1988) estimates that 20% to 25% of sons (and 5% of daughters) of alcoholics become alcoholics themselves. Both rates are four to five times the rate of the general population. He distinguishes between "familial" and "nonfamilial" alcoholics. Familial alcoholics begin drinking earlier and develop a more severe form of alcoholism than nonfamilial alcoholics. The latter group may drink to self-medicate problems such as anxiety and depression.

Relapse may be more likely to result in familial alcoholics because of their high degree of dependence, as indicated by tremulousness, morning drinking, and blackouts. Higher levels of dependence have been associated with continuing alcohol problems (Polich, Armor, & Braiker, 1981) and perceived dangerousness of potential relapse situations (Litman, Eiser, Rawson, & Oppenheim, 1977). However, dependence is not a clear mediator of relapse since it does not predict attrition from treatment, consumption at follow-up, or duration of aftercare involvement (Kivlahan, Sher, & Donovan, 1989). Objective symptoms of dependence may be *less* predictive of relapse than subjective judgments (Heather, Rollnick, & Wilson, 1983).

There has been little direct evaluation of the relationship between familial alcoholism and outcome. Krippenstapel (1988) found that patients with at least one parent and one sibling who were alcoholic were 1.5 times more likely to relapse during a 12-month follow-up than those with no family history of alcoholism. This study was exploratory and examined socially stable patients, so conclusions are tentative. To make more valid conclusions, evaluations of dependency should be part of a multidimensional assessment. This finding suggests a psychological, rather than a biological, predisposition to relapse.

Neurological/Neuropsychological Impairments Neurological impairments of alcoholics may be viewed as determinants or consequences. Some researchers consider certain alcoholics to have been neurologically compromised prior to actual alcohol use (Tarter & Alterman, 1984). Begleiter, Porjesz,

Bihari, and Kissin (1984) studied P300 brain waves in high-risk boys. These waves are thought to measure one's ability to identify relevant stimuli and therefore aid in evaluating behavior. The researchers found decreased amplitude in these boys compared to controls and hypothesized that this difficulty enhances the probability of later drinking. Tarter, Hegedus, and Gavaler (1985) suggest a higher probability of hyperkinesis in high-risk children. Schuckit (1987) reports that high-risk adolescents report less subjective intoxication following a moderate dose of alcohol. These factors would support findings of poor problem-solving in alcoholics, which may increase the risk of relapse (Cooper, Russell, & George, 1988). However, neurological and neuropsychological deficits could result from a variety of influences, including head injury secondary to physical abuse by alcoholic parents (Searles, 1988).

These deficits can also be seen as consequences of alcohol abuse. The pattern of cognitive dysfunctions in early recovery is well established (Wilkinson & Sanchez-Craig, 1981). Approximately 75% to 95% of recovering alcoholics demonstrate brain dysfunctions (Porjesz & Begleiter, 1983). These dysfunctions may be manifested in difficulty with abstract concepts (how many alcoholics understand spirituality in the early phases of recovery?), problem-solving (how many alcoholics in early recovery evaluate a range of options before making decisions?), and learning new associations (how much of what they have been taught do alcoholics in early recovery recall?). Well-practiced skills such as general knowledge and verbal abilities usually remain intact.

Several authors report that a lesser degree of these impairments is related to a longer abstinence (Abbott & Gregson, 1981), better postdischarge functioning (Walker, Donovan, Kivlahan, & O'Leary, 1983), better participation in rehabilitation programs (O'Leary, Donovan, Chaney, & Walker, 1979; Parsons, 1987), and higher clinician ratings of prognosis (Leber, Parsons, & Nichols, 1985). There is some controversy as to their ability to predict relapse, but clinicians need to be aware that these difficulties can interfere with treatment (McCrady & Smith, 1986).

Others have attempted to define these deficits as a syndrome beginning in early recovery. As stated earlier, Gorski and Miller (1986) used the term *postacute withdrawal.* Prior to this conceptualization, Wellman (1954) coined the term *late withdrawal symptoms* which included irritability, depression, insomnia, fatigue, restlessness, aloneness, and distractibility. This constellation of symptoms has also been labeled *intermediate brain syndrome* (Bennett, 1960) or *protracted withdrawal syndrome* (Kissin, 1979).

No precisely and empirically defined syndrome exists at present, but there is little doubt that a variety of cognitive symptoms appear in early recovery and diminish over time (usually a period of months or even years). Mossberg, Liljeberg, and Borg (1985), referring to an alcoholic subacute protracted withdrawal syndrome, found sleep problems, depressive symptoms, concentration problems, anxiety, and failing memory for 4 to 8 weeks following acute withdrawal. DeSoto, O'Donnell, Allred, and Lopes (1985) studied a sample of alcoholics with up to 10 years of abstinence. They found that a high proportion of alcoholics in early recovery experience sleep problems, difficulty remembering things, trouble concentrating, thought blocking, and unpleasant thoughts. With continued abstinence over several years, measures of health and psychological functioning gradually improved to essentially normal levels.

Recent studies suggest that drug users experience similar symptoms, labeled as "post-drug impairment syndrome" (PDIS) by Tennant (1988). According to Tennant, drug abuse may damage receptor sites and/or neurotransmitter metabolism in the brain, resulting in poor self-care, difficulties enduring stress, problems with memory and attention, temper tantrums, and alienation from society.

These findings suggest that a patient's neurological and neuropsychological conditions are potentially important factors in the relapse process. Poor cognitive functioning may impair the integration of treatment information, problem-solving abilities, and development of social support necessary for relapse prevention.

Cue Reactivity Wikler (1948) reported on opiate addicts who returned to New York City after a period of abstinence. Upon experiencing the sights and sounds of the city, they would feel the symptoms of opiate withdrawal. This feeling was so intense that some would become nauseated or vomit. The craving to inject heroin would build until they gave in and became readdicted.

Ludwig and Wikler (1974) used such observations to generate a theory of relapse based on classical conditioning principles. Craving is a psychological manifestation of a *subclinical conditioned withdrawal syndrome,* a term indicating that stimuli connected to withdrawal become triggers for later alcohol or drug use. If the alcoholic or addict is exposed to these triggers after a period of abstinence, withdrawal reactions are aroused and the possibility of relapse increases. These triggers could include liquor bottles, drug paraphernalia, pictures or movies of drug use, drug-using friends, songs, or even conversations about alcohol or drug use (also known as "war stories").

Researchers have found that physiological responses give clues about such cue reactivity. Alcoholics exposed to alcohol cues have shown increased pupillary dilation (Kennedy, 1971), physiological arousal (Kaplan, Meyer, & Stroebel, 1983), and salivation (Monti et al., 1987). Childress, McLellan, Ehrman, and O'Brien (1988) demonstrated that abstinent opioid addicts continue to exhibit physiological arousal even after 30 days of residential treatment. Pilot data with abstinent cocaine addicts revealed similar findings. Finally, smokers exposed to smoking cues show more heart rate increases than nonsmokers or successful abstainers exposed to the same cues (Abrams et al., 1987).

Cue reactivity therefore seems to be related to relapse potential (Niaura et al., 1988). While there are certainly physical correlates related to craving, research indicates that behavioral and cognitive aspects also need to be considered. Mood states, coping skills, and positive or negative thinking are critical in understanding craving (Niaura et al., 1988).

Biochemical Deficiencies Several researchers have advanced theories that alcoholics and drug addicts possess biochemical abnormalities that increase the risk of relapse. Dole and Nyswander (1967) postulated a *metabolic deficiency* hypothesis with heroin addicts, which held that repeated exposure to narcotic drugs induces metabolic changes that can be corrected through substitution of methadone. Later, Trachtenberg and Blum (1987) suggested that both alcoholics and heroin addicts may lack endorphins (endogenous opiates). These authors suggest that tetrahydroisoquinolines (TIQs), which are opiate-like metabolites of alcohol, may produce a false sense of well-being, thus encouraging further drinking. When infused into the brains of monkeys, TIQs can induce drinking binges (J. Wallace, 1989).

The biochemical equation may be mediated by internal levels of stimulation. Zuckerman (1986) found a relationship between sensation seeking and drug use that is possibly mediated by levels of gonadal hormones, monoamine oxidase, and other neurotransmitters. Sensation seeking is related to alcohol use in young adult alcoholics (Schwarz, Burkhart, & Green, 1978). Polydrug users score higher in this dimension than do depressant users (Galizio & Stein, 1983).

Perhaps alcoholics have a low internal level of arousal that they try to correct through stimulation seeking with alcohol. In recovering alcoholics, Borg, Czarnecka, Kvande, Mossberg, and Sedvall (1983) found a decrease in noradrenaline (a stimulating neurotransmitter) to lower than normal levels by the third through the sixth months of recovery. Not only is relapse a high probability during this phase, but many alcoholics also compensate for this lack with large amounts of caffeine and nicotine.

Cocaine addicts often experience "crashes" after they complete cocaine binges. The symptoms include lack of energy, headaches, irritability, excessive sleeping, and craving. These symptoms have been linked to a depletion of dopamine (Dackis, Gold, & Pottash, 1987), which may result in a vicious cycle of overstimulation followed by exhaustion of reward systems in the brain. Desipramine (an antidepressant) and bromocriptine (which stimulates postsynaptic receptors the same way cocaine does) have been hypothesized to reduce craving and block euphoria. It may be possible, therefore, to prevent relapse by balancing neurotransmitter levels.

The biochemical explanations for alcoholism and other drug use remain highly speculative at this time. As Wallace (1988) states, "Recent neurobiological research is most complex and generalizations are hazardous" (p. 208). He points out that the lack of replication, response differences across animals, doses, and brain locations, and difficulties in correlating metabolites with brain chemistry suggest the need for further study. In addition, the level of metabolites is affected by the presence of other drugs in the system (Chang, Kwon, Hamada, & Yahiku, 1990). Because 20% to 80% of alcoholic populations use other nonmedically prescribed substances (Newcomb & Bentler, 1986), conclusions made without controlling for multiple drug usage are questionable.

The application of these findings to clinical care is even less clear and may actually result in risky interventions. Treatments based on notions such as the metabolic deficiency hypothesis have received little empirical support and may actually encourage dependence on addicting substances such as methadone (Bratter, Pennacchia, & Gauya, 1985).

Psychological Risk Factors

Expectancies Three sets of alcohol expectancies are critical to understanding relapse: (a) beliefs about preferred substance, (b) beliefs about treatment and self-help, and (c) beliefs about relapse and recovery. These beliefs draw an "if–then" connection between certain conditions and possible consequences, meaning that if condition A is present, then consequence B will occur. The research in this area is voluminous; only some of the pertinent findings are summarized here.

Most available research has evaluated expectancies about alcohol. These expectancies have been referred to as the "Seven Dwarves," since alcoholics are often asked whether drinking makes them grumpy, sleepy, dopey, bashful, and so on (Leigh, 1989a). Expectancies of improved social functioning can predict which adolescents are more likely to progress to adult drinking patterns at 1- to 2-year follow-up (Christiansen, Roehling, Smith, & Goldman, 1989). The tendency for much of the increase in positive expectancies to occur in the third and fourth grades is particularly troubling (Miller, Smith, & Goldman, 1990).

Beliefs about the effects of alcohol on behavior and emotions can motivate drinking in alcoholics (Brown, Goldman, & Christiansen, 1985). Less experienced drinkers tend to hold global, undifferentiated views of alcohol effects, while more experienced drinkers refine their expectations into more concrete factors (Brown, Goldman, Inn, & Anderson, 1980). Positive expectancies about alcohol also increase the risk of relapse (Brown, 1985). These findings suggest powerful effects of beliefs and attitudes on self-reported alcohol consumption. However, the clinician needs to consider the population, the connection between expectancy and *actual* consumption, and even the beverage type when making an assessment (Leigh, 1989a).

Beliefs about treatment and self-help are critical to both compliance and effectiveness in treatment. The dropout rate from alcoholism programs is between 28% and 80% within the first month of treatment (Rees, 1985). In lifestyle change programs involving obesity, smoking, and stress management, the dropout rate ranges from 20% to 80% (Martin & Dubbert, 1986). Among the major culprits are uncertainties about the efficacy of treatment, past negative experiences with health care providers, impatience with the progress of treatment, competing environmental demands, and the individual's desire to maintain control over various domains of his or her life (Meichenbaum & Turk, 1987). These variables have not been widely studied in relation to relapse, but there are many anecdotal reports of negative treatment experiences and incomplete orientations to treatment. I have heard alcoholics and addicts express bewilderment about therapists who "didn't talk." The treatment of such an impulsive population requires a directive and knowledgeable stance, especially since they often have doubt about whether their addictions are understood.

Beliefs about relapse and recovery constitute a third important (but relatively ignored) area. Eastman and Norris (1982) indicated that both alcoholics and their counselors predicted their relapses at a 75% accuracy rate. These authors considered self-identity to be important, suggesting that alcoholics drink because they prefer the version of themselves that exists during drinking. They may have in memory an overly positive picture of themselves (a phenomenon known as "euphoric recall"). On the other hand, dysfunctional behaviors such as dwelling on negative situations, avoiding problems, and feeling doomed by the past have been associated with addiction severity and urges to drink (Rohsenow et al., 1989). In fact, "feeling doomed" was the best predictor of frequency and average quantity of alcohol consumption at follow-up.

Taken together, expectancies about the effects of drugs and alcohol, treatment, and relapse can be significant factors in recovery. Although further refinements of these expectancies are needed, evaluating the patient's belief system is clearly an integral part of relapse prevention.

Coping Skills and Stressful Challenges The relationship between alcohol use, anxiety, and stress is complicated. Alcohol has been shown variously to reduce, increase, and have no effect on anxiety (Steele & Josephs, 1988). Swaim, Oetting, Edwards, and Beauvais (1989) found virtually no relationship between emotional distress and drug use in adolescents.

When alcohol use *is* related to stress, cognitive impairment rather than the physiological effect of alcohol may be the deciding factor (Steele, Southwick, & Pagano, 1986). Alcohol limits the amount of information that can be processed and narrows perception to most immediate internal and external stimuli. As a result, one's comprehension of total reality diminishes so that more remote (and probably crucial) problems recede in importance. The drinker then perceives this reaction as a reduction in stress. If, however, the problems are present during the drinking episode, they may become catastrophized (the "crying in my beer" phenomenon) and lead to an experience of *increased* stress or anxiety.

When faced with such limited perceptions, addicted people often revert to overlearned behavior patterns connected to their primary addictions. Relapsers tend to score lower in measures of coping with difficult situations (Rosenberg, 1983). Among smokers, those who use more than one coping strategy are more likely to remain abstinent (Bliss, Garvey, Heinhold, & Hitchcock, 1989). Among dieters, those who combine cognitive and behavioral coping strategies are less likely to resort to overeating (Grilo, Schiffman, & Wing, 1989).

Schiffman (1988) delineates a variety of coping skills derived from smokers. Behavioral coping strategies include developing alternative consumptions or activities, self-care, avoidance of high-risk stimuli, controlled usage, and self-reward. Cognitive coping strategies include self-reminders about consequences, "self-talk," goal setting, distraction, relaxing imagery, and self-punitive thoughts. There is little specific data about the effectiveness of these methods, but self-punitive thoughts ("You fool, you started again") and willpower seem to be relatively ineffective in reducing relapse.

Among coping strategies, communication and refusal skills may be the most prominent. Nancy Reagan's "Just Say No" campaign several years ago focused on refusal skills. Despite the simplicity of this campaign, it is known that deficits in social competence may predispose adolescents to abusive drinking and nicotine use (Monti, Abrams, Kadden, & Cooney, 1989). Poor refusal skills, difficulties expressing emotion, and limited communication skills may increase the risk of substance abuse. Interventions that build these skills may help teenagers avoid substance abuse.

Studies designed to show a link between global social skills deficits and substance abuse have produced some positive but inconclusive findings (Chiauzzi, in press; Monti, Abrams, Binkoff, & Zwick, 1986). Wills, Baker, and Botvin (1989) found that social and dating assertiveness actually correlate *positively* with substance use among adolescents, while "substance-specific" assertiveness was negatively associated with substance use. A study by Abrams et al. (cited in Monti, Abrams, Kadden, & Cooney, 1989) required alcoholics to role-play actual drinking situations. Results suggested that alcoholics are less socially competent than nonalcoholics. Social skills deficits have also been linked to relapse (Marlatt & Gordon, 1985).

Social skills treatments aimed at improving drink refusal, appropriate anger expression, and coping with anxiety have shown a modest degree of success in reducing drinking and building social competence (Chiauzzi, in press; Monti et al., 1986). These skills decay over time, however, and may not necessarily be reflected in reduced use of most drugs (Hawkins, Catalano, Gillmore, & Wells, 1989). The use of booster sessions may enhance these results.

In summary, it appears that coping skills are central to the recovery process. There is little evidence supporting the contention that all alcoholics and addicts lack a *particular* coping skill, for example, assertiveness. Instead, clinicians should assess a variety of coping skills, since each patient will have different strengths and weaknesses.

Psychopathology Most addicted people have addiction as their primary and only diagnosis. However, a significant portion of alcoholics and drug addicts fit criteria for additional psychiatric diagnoses. Hesselbrock, Meyer, and Keener (1985) found that 77% of patients in a sample of alcoholics met lifetime criteria for DSM-III (*Diagnostic and Statistical Manual of Mental Disorders,* 3rd ed.) axis I or II diagnoses. Ross, Glaser, and Germanson (1988) found similar results in that 78% of alcoholics and drug addicts met lifetime criteria for psychiatric disorders, while 65% had a current psychiatric disorder. Ninety-five percent of those who used both alcohol and drugs met lifetime criteria. Mirin, Weiss, Michael, and Griffin (1988) found a 40% rate of nondrug diagnoses in a mixed sample of substance abusers. Severity of substance dependence is the best predictor of psychiatric disturbance (Ross et al., 1988).

The most common concurrent diagnoses associated with substance abuse are affective, anxiety, and antisocial personality disorders (other personality disorders are found to a much lesser extent). In their alcoholic and drug addicted sample, Ross et al. (1988) found that 27%, 33%, and 37%, respectively, met these criteria. Mirin et al. (1988) report similar findings with opiate, stimulant, and depressant abusers. Lifetime estimates of schizophrenia are in the 10% to 15% range (Ross et al., 1988; Solomon, 1989). Of these disorders, antisocial personality and depression are most likely to be present after 1 year of sobriety (Penick, Powell, Liskow, Jackson, & Nickel, 1988).

The presence of particular psychiatric problems can differentially affect treatment outcome. Schuckit (1985) found that primary alcoholics had a better outcome than alcoholics with a primary diagnosis of drug abuse or antisocial personality. Rounsaville, Dolinsky, Babor, and Meyer (1987) reported that male and female alcoholics with additional diagnoses of antisocial personality and drug abuse did more poorly than those with alcoholism alone. However, women who also had major depression showed a *better* outcome while men showed a poorer prognosis. Hatsukami,

Pickens, and Svikis (1981) found that relapsed subjects had higher mean depression scores than abstinent subjects at follow-up.

Woody, McLellan, Luborsky, and O'Brien (1985) found that methadone-maintained opiate addicts with antisocial personalities were doing more poorly at 7-month follow-up than those without the additional diagnosis. Kosten, Kosten, and Rounsaville (1989) found an 80% rate of personality disorders in opiate addicts. Those diagnosed as borderline personalities had significantly more alcoholism at 2.5-year follow-up than those without personality disorders. Antisocial personalities did not differ from other personality disorders in long-term outcome from opiate abuse; they simply engaged in more illegal activities.

Few studies have separated "true" antisocial behavior (predating addiction) from antisocial behavior symptomatic of substance use. It is therefore difficult to make conclusions about the effects of this behavior on treatment outcome (Gerstley, Alterman, McLellan, & Woody, 1990). However, one would expect "symptomatic" psychopaths to have a better treatment response than "true" psychopaths.

The relationship between alcoholism and anxiety disorders is equally complex. A recent review by Kushner, Sher, and Beitman (1990) suggests that with agoraphobia and social phobia, alcohol problems tend to arise as a result of attempts at self-medication. Panic disorder and generalized anxiety tend to follow from pathological drinking. Simple phobia does not appear to be related to alcohol problems. In terms of outcome, global deficits such as agoraphobia and social phobia would be more likely to persist and possibly contribute to a higher potential for relapse.

There is evidence that global psychiatric severity can affect the potential for relapse also. Rounsaville et al. (1987) reported generally poorer outcomes with the presence of coexisting psychiatric problems. McLellan, Luborsky, Woody, O'Brien, and Druley (1983) reviewed patient improvements at 6-month follow-up for six treatment programs (including therapeutic communities, methadone maintenance, outpatient treatment, and inpatient rehabilitation). They found that patients with low psychiatric severity improved in every treatment program. Patients at moderate levels of severity improved when treatment was matched to their needs (e.g., those with serious family or employment problems did better in inpatient programs). Patients with high severity showed almost no improvement in any treatment program.

These studies provide clear indications that psychiatric severity needs to be accounted for, particularly with regard to selection of treatment regimens. Psychiatric severity represents one of the more robust predictors of relapse.

A Word About the Addictive Personality A comprehensive discussion of addictive personality research is beyond the scope of this book. Babor and

Lauerman (1986) report that 139 different typologies of alcoholics were devised between 1850 and 1941. Personality research with alcoholics was summed up by Mark Keller (cited in Goodwin, 1988): "The investigation of any trait in alcoholics will show that they either had more or less of it" (p. 133).

Researchers now accept the hypothesis that alcoholism and drug abuse have multiple sources and that treatment can no longer be based on the theory of a singular alcoholic personality (Graham & Strenger, 1988). Despite findings that traits such as sensation seeking, field dependence (relying on external stimuli to form perceptions), external locus of control (feeling that forces are beyond one's control), and stimulus reduction (using alcohol to reduce pain) may be related to existing alcoholism (Cox, 1986), no single trait *predicts* alcoholism or relapse with any consistency. The same can be said of other addictive behaviors, such as opiate abuse (Sutker & Allain, 1988). In fact, there does not appear to be any motivational process unique to addiction: The same motivations drive responses to pharmacologic and nonpharmacologic stimuli ("Addictive Personality," 1990).

Instead, it appears that *behavior* provides a better basis for predicting alcoholism. Children or adolescents are predisposed to alcoholism when they exhibit an excessive activity level, high emotionality, or antisocial behaviors (Tarter, 1988). It is antisocial *behavior* (rejection of society's rules), not antisocial personality, that predicts future alcoholism (Nathan, 1988). Minnesota Multiphasic Personality Inventory (MMPI) data reveal that alcoholics are impulsive, have low frustration tolerance, and control their anger poorly, but there is no single profile type that characterizes *all* alcoholics (Graham & Strenger, 1988).

Social Risk Factors

Life Events Rudolf Moos and his colleagues (Billings & Moos, 1983; Cronkite & Moos, 1980; Finney, Moos, & Mewborn, 1980; Moos, Finney, & Chan, 1981) conducted a series of studies demonstrating the powerful effects that life events (such as moving, changing jobs, separation from a spouse, or financial problems) exert on recovery. Billings and Moos (1980) found that negative life events such as the death of a friend or economic problems were more prevalent in relapsed alcoholics. These individuals reported twice as many negative events and half as many positive events as recovered alcoholics. Cronkite and Moos (1980) found that stressful life events have an influence on depression which may lead to relapse. Finney et al. (1980) reported that negative life events were related to poor outcome, but that positive events were not. Finally, Moos et al. (1981) found that relapsed alcoholics experienced fewer positive and greater negative life events than community controls or recovered alcoholics.

Overall, these studies suggest that life events, especially negative ones, are strongly related to outcome. The relationship between drinking and life events should not be considered a one-way street; they affect each other.

Socioeconomic Status Baekland (1977) distinguished "good prognosis" (higher socioeconomic status [SES] and social stability) from "bad prognosis" (skid row) alcoholics on the basis of dramatic differences in range of outcome: 32%–68% versus 0%–18%, respectively. Better alcoholism treatment outcomes have also been associated with higher status occupations (skilled, white collar, professional) and higher personal or family income (Westermeyer, 1989).

Educational level, on the other hand, has received mixed reviews as a predictor of outcome. Some studies show better education to be a predictor of success (Baekland, Lundwall, & Kissin, 1975) while others find that it fails to discriminate treatment responders and nonresponders (Ornstein & Cherepon, 1985).

Higher socioeconomic levels may assist in the recovery process, as long as the patient utilizes his resources. However, economic and educational advantages provide little help if they are used to deny the negative consequences of addictive behavior. Whether a person is advantaged or disadvantaged, the major concern is his ability to apply whatever resources are available to his recovery.

Marital and Family Cohesion Bromet and Moos (1977) reported that married patients and widowed patients fared better in treatment than single, separated, or divorced patients. Westermeyer's (1989) review of this variable suggests that being married has been consistently related to positive treatment outcome in studies over the past 20 years. Furthermore, poor family cohesion, exemplified by a lack of expressiveness and the presence of conflict, is found more frequently in relapsed alcoholics (Billings & Moos, 1983). Finney, Moos, and Mewborn (1980) found that an active recreational orientation, joint performance of household tasks, and low conflict improved prognosis. This finding has been replicated with opiate addicts. The length of time an addict is drug free is correlated highly with family leadership, closeness between spouses, a nonhostile mood, empathy, and efficient problem solving (Kosten, Jalali, Steidl, & Kleber, 1987).

Stable social support is another robust predictor of relapse. Improving family communication, decreasing conflict, and developing activities that compete with substance use should be primary goals in relapse prevention.

Employment Being employed consistently enhances treatment outcome with alcoholics (Bromet & Moos, 1977; Ornstein & Cherepon, 1987). This finding has been replicated with opiate addicts (Stephens & Cottrell, 1972). In addition, the work environment appears to play a role in relapse. Billings and Moos (1983) found that relapsed alcoholics report significantly more time pressure on the job. These authors also reported that involvement in work and cohesive relationships with coworkers contributed to treatment success. However, the quality of the work environment does not seem as critical for individuals who have returned to their families (Finney, Moos, & Mewborn, 1980). Families may act as a buffer against potential negative factors outside the home. For those addicted individuals who identify primarily with their jobs, intervention in the work environment will be central to relapse prevention.

Residential Stability Living with others has been shown to have a mild relationship with outcome (Westermeyer, 1989). McCance and McCance (1969) reported improved outcomes for those living with a spouse, friend, or relative. Bromet and Moos (1977) noted a strong effect on posttreatment performance for alcoholics living with their spouses. Finally, being homeless is particularly indicative of poor prognosis (Poikolanien & Saila, 1986).

Taken together, these findings suggest that merely living with someone does not provide a buffer against relapse (particularly if that person is an active alcoholic or addict). Living arrangements become a significant relapse predictor when the individual is homeless.

THE ISSUE OF MOTIVATION

In his exhaustive review of motivation for treatment, Miller (1985) states, "A client tends to be judged as motivated if he or she accepts the therapist's view of the problem (including the need for help and the diagnosis), is distressed, and complies with treatment prescriptions" (pp. 87–88). Motivation is typically regarded as something inherent in the alcoholic or addict, a trait that is independent of outside influences. Comments such as "He hasn't hit bottom yet," "He doesn't hurt enough," and "He's not ready" all imply that the alcoholic needs to develop some internal force that will impel him toward treatment. However, a stated willingness to participate in treatment is unrelated to outcome (Orford & Hawker, 1974).

Motivation is often in the eye of the beholder (the counselor or therapist) and is also a function of therapist behaviors. Therapist hostility, making a poor prognosis, and lack of empathy can all detract from treatment outcome (Miller, 1985). Confrontation, thought to be a cornerstone of effective treatment for addictions, can precipitate dropout, negative emotional states, lowered self-esteem, and eventual relapse (Miller & Hester, 1986). Motivation therefore appears to be an interactional rather than an individual phenomenon.

Some try to increase the alcoholic's motivation through legal or nonlegal coercion. Legal coercion in the form of forced A.A. attendance after conviction of driving while intoxicated has been shown to enhance compliance only during the probation period (Rosenberg & Liftik, 1976). With people who have little to lose by complying (such as skid row alcoholics), coercion does no better than voluntary treatment (Westermeyer, 1989).

Similar results have been obtained for nonlegal coercion. Freedberg and Johnston (1980) compared coerced and noncoerced alcoholics 12 months after treatment. There were no differences in groups in employment status, work productivity, abstinence from alcohol, absenteeism, or tardiness. No matter what kind of coercion is used, there seems to be no difference in outcome between coerced and voluntary patients (Miller, 1985).

The patient's goals also need to be entered into the motivational equation. Some patients seek unconditional abstinence ("I'll never drink again"), while others endorse a more conditional approach ("I will seek total abstinence, but realize that there is always the possibility of a slip"). Marlatt and Gordon (1985) predicted a better outcome for the latter group. However, Hall, Havassy, and Wasserman (1990) found that 43% of those with the unconditional goal eventually relapsed, while 77% of subjects who accepted the possibility of slips eventually relapsed. This finding disputes the Marlatt and Gordon (1985) prediction, but further research into the framing of recovery goals is needed.

SUMMARY

Taken together, the above findings provide strong support for a biopsychosocial interpretation of addiction and relapse. The biopsychosocial assumption that each domain interacts with the others is borne out by findings in cue reactivity, severity, and psychopathology. In each of these areas, biological factors are mediated by perceptions. Social and coping skills can affect one's decision making in selecting environments, which can then trigger craving. Demographic and family factors can relate to a sense of belonging and provide a foundation for a successful recovery.

Still lacking is the ability to determine the relative contribution of these factors for individuals. Current technology does not make this possible, but clinicians can make educated guesses by systematically evaluating biological, psychological, and social domains. The next chapter presents a discussion of assessment techniques applicable to a biopsychosocial viewpoint.

Chapter 5

Assessment of Relapse Potential

Do not look where you fell but where you slipped.
—African proverb

As mentioned earlier, many patients approach relapse as if it were an unexpected event. Some expect a metamorphosis in recovery and become surprised that it is a day-to-day, gradual process that moves along in barely perceptible increments. They seek a global personality change but eventually realize that they will have to settle for lesser (but still significant) changes in thoughts, behaviors, emotions, and relationships. Those in recovery who make a careful self-assessment in the absence of substances position themselves better for more enduring changes. It is the job of the clinician to help the alcoholic or addict maintain accurate self-assessments that promote these changes.

This chapter addresses factors that need to be assessed prior to initiating relapse prevention interventions. To date, relapse prevention assessment has not been fully systematized, as each major approach has targeted a different aspect of recovery. Since relapse represents an incomplete assessment (Monti, Abrams, Kadden, & Cooney, 1989), the assessment process described here targets biological, psychological, and social risk factors for each patient. The patient is considered an active participant in the assessment process.

The assessment suggested in this chapter is based primarily on the empirical findings reviewed in the previous chapter. However, my experience with relapsed alcoholics and addicts has yielded other fruitful avenues of evaluation that will be included in this biopsychosocial risk assessment. The following assessment process can be utilized for treatment selection and matching purposes. Each section will be described in greater detail later in the chapter. We will begin with ways in which the clinician can enhance information gathering.

ASSESSMENT STYLE

In his article, "The Art of Being a Failure as a Therapist," Jay Haley (1969) cautions against the following therapist behaviors:

Be Passive

Be Inactive

Be Reflective

Be Silent

Beware

These cautions, originally applied to traditional psychotherapy, also apply to the assessment of relapse potential. In a field where treatment encourages patients to "keep it simple" (avoid overanalyzing problems), it is not unusual for relapsed alcoholics and addicts to offer the most immediate explanations that come to mind. If a clinician simply accepts excuses such as "I forgot to go to my A.A. meetings" or "I found myself with a drink in my hand," he or she will probably repeat suggestions already made without exploring the many factors that can lead to relapse. This form of passive acceptance tends to increase the probability of future relapses.

On the other hand, forcing acceptance of A.A. participation, counseling, or psychiatric labels will only increase an addict's resistance. Expecting people to accept unilateral opinions without question is unrealistic. Confronting people who already feel defeated may increase their feelings of guilt and shame. Limiting options may result in only superficial behavior change—if even this is accomplished. Under these conditions, assessment is a coercive process.

Instead, I advocate a cooperative effort in which therapist and patient both explore factors in relapse. To this process therapists can offer a range of formal assessment instruments and clinical judgments. The patient can offer subjective and experiential information. Most important, the therapist is modeling a process of assessment that the patient can use in his natural environment. As relapse is considered here to be "incomplete assessment," a more complete evaluation is essential in avoiding relapse. With the type of exploration suggested here, the patient is being taught a more comprehensive way of evaluating his or her recovery.

As important as knowing what to do is knowing what not to do. The following is a recipe for therapist failure:

1. Force the patient to accept the labels "alcoholic" or "addict" before understanding what they mean.
2. Present as few options as possible.
3. Confront the patient, *no matter what.*
4. Use scare tactics and other extreme statements.
5. Meet denial with argumentation.
6. Present unilateral treatment goals.
7. Force conclusions and interpretations.

BIOPSYCHOSOCIAL RISK ANALYSIS

Risk factors can be assessed best through a systematic assessment of the following areas: (a) historical factors (family history, relapse history, treatment history, self-help history, and substitute addictions), (b) biological risk factors (dependence, craving/cue reactivity, sensation seeking, and health factors), (c) psychological factors (expectancy, coping skills, personality, and psychopathology), and (d) social factors (stability of relationships and environment). The clinician who carefully interviews the addicted person or the client's significant others will often unearth information that was kept secret or considered unimportant by the relapser. The clinician's main tasks are to emphasize the significance of this information to the patient and to develop interventions that address high-risk factors.

Historical Factors

Family History A client's family history is important for three reasons: (a) to assess substance abuse patterns and relapse/recovery trends in other family members, (b) to assess the possibility of a dual diagnosis, and (c) to assess potential substitute addictions. The substance abuse and recovery patterns of family members are often reflected in the patient's own patterns, especially in the patient's philosophy about recovery. For instance, if the patient's father was an addict who became abstinent without formal treatment or participation in A.A., the patient may attempt to maintain the same self-reliant attitude. Such individuals may resist suggestions or avoid help seeking.

Psychiatric disorders present in family members may not have been expressed yet in the patient because of self-medication or age factors. When the patient becomes abstinent, there may be a tendency for these disorders (e.g., depression) to appear. Identifying this potential may help prevent a relapse in the patient and prepare a treatment regimen that can address the additional disorder.

Potential substitute addictions can also be present in family members. Relatives may have resorted to these addictions as replacements for the ones they were trying to avoid. These addictions may also suggest possibilities that the patient has not yet tried. For instance, if a recovering cocaine addict has a father who is a compulsive gambler, it is important to try to determine the possibilities that the patient might turn to gambling in early recovery.

Relapse History A patient's relapse history provides valuable clues about his or her potential for relapse. The drugs abused, the pattern of usage, abstinent periods, and precipitants of relapse all need to be assessed. In evaluating these patterns, the "career" aspects of addiction become obvious. As in occupational careers, there are fluctuations, shifts, and changes in interests in addiction careers. Few addicted individuals maintain unchanging patterns over the course of many years. The drugs they use, environmental circumstances, interpersonal influences, their physical health, and their emotional makeup all undergo transformations.

The factors that influence these shifts may be reintroduced in a more systematic manner if they previously led to abstinence. For instance, some alcoholics relapse when they live alone and remain sober if they are living with others. Another example is that many women are able to remain abstinent when they are pregnant but revert to substance use soon after delivery. Recreating the cognitive and emotional factors that led to these successes can decrease the potential for relapse. To display the patterning of relapses, a relapse timeline (see Appendix A) can be used. To use the timeline patients blacken in periods in which they were abstinent. From the emerging pattern, clues about the effects of time of year, holidays, and anniversaries may become evident. A gradual shortening of abstinent periods over time suggests a progression of the addiction, while a lengthening suggests that the patient is learning but still needs guidance.

Treatment History A patient's treatment history provides information about his or her help-seeking and knowledge of available resources. Careful questioning will reveal how the patient regards particular modalities, therapist styles, and theoretical approaches. The assumption that the patient is a passive vessel into which treatment information can be poured is questionable. Instead, he or she actively perceives (and perhaps inaccurately translates) various interventions. Patients have a sense of what is effective and can often use this information to become active participants in the treatment process.

In addition, self-reports of past treatment may suggest biases that influence expectations about current treatment. Of particular importance are personal issues that were *not* previously discussed in treatment. Posttraumatic stress, sexual and physical abuse, and unresolved interpersonal problems are sensitive areas that are frequently avoided unless the therapist carefully evaluates their potential contribution to relapse. In many cases, unresolved feelings surface only *after* a period of abstinence. These unresolved feelings may not necessarily be linked to the original stressor(s), but may manifest themselves as unstable behavior, depression, floating anxiety, or hopelessness.

Self-Help History The popularity of the "Minnesota Model" (an A.A. focus through the usage of recovering counselors) makes an analysis of self-help patterns essential. Combined with a treatment approach that builds responsibility and self-efficacy, A.A. can be a beneficial and rewarding experience for many recovering individuals. The feedback provided at A.A. meetings can prevent "apparently irrelevant decisions" (Marlatt & Gordon, 1985) which precede relapse. Lack of sponsorship, minimal involvement within meetings, and negative reactions to suggestions can all disrupt this feedback mechanism.

A disbelief in the A.A. philosophy should not result in confrontation but rather in an exploration of the patient's philosophy of growth and change. The patient can be asked to indicate which items in the "Tools of Recovery" list (see Table 5.1) he or she finds difficult to believe or perform. Troublesome items can also be potential indicators of a developing relapse.

Substitute Addictions

The biopsychosocial approach requires a comprehensive assessment of all addictions. I have chosen the term *substitute addictions* to signify the potential for recovering people to find new addictions while abstaining from their primary drug(s). However, substitute addictions may also coexist quietly with the treated addiction and emerge as a primary addiction in recovery.

The recovery process is evidenced when a patient recognizes the potential danger inherent in these alternative addictions. Such substitutions are particularly troublesome if they are used for effects similar to those produced by the original drugs of abuse. Any indication of other addictive behaviors may require additional assessment. This can be accomplished through use of available questionnaires and interview schedules. Table 5.2 lists appropriate assessments for each major addiction.

Table 5.1. Tools of Recovery

Biological	Psychological	Social
Maintain good nutritional and exercise habits	Remember your last drunk	Develop social support
Get plenty of sleep	Learn to cope with anger and depression	Seek feedback from others
Get treatment for physical ailments	Build moderation into your life	Avoid judging yourself and others
Keep organized to keep your thinking clear	Keep an open mind	Avoid drinking and drugging relationships
Follow doctors' prescription orders	Replace guilt with gratitude	Share your pain
Remember that withdrawal may take several months	Keep track of your relapse triggers	Let people know how you feel
Avoid abusive use of caffeine and nicotine	Change old routines	Do not expect people to read your mind
Do not let craving control your behavior	Avoid testing your willpower	Accept responsibility for your actions
Learn to relax	Eliminate self-pity	Remember that you are not alone

Biological Risk Analysis

Dependence Dependence itself appears to be a moderate-to-weak predictor of relapse, but this is not surprising because dependence may function in two ways. First, some highly dependent alcoholics and addicts may relapse more readily because of the strong physical "pull" of the substance or the difficulty with disengaging from an addictive lifestyle. Second, the highly dependent alcoholic or addict may relapse *less* readily because of the difficulty of maintaining denial in the face of serious consequences. As a result, dependence should be assessed carefully, because *it may be predictive for particular individuals.* When combined with expectancy, it can be highly predictive. For a more complete assessment, the Addiction Severity Index (McLellan, O'Brien, Kron, Alterman, & Druley, 1980) or the Alcohol Dependence Scale (Skinner & Allen, 1982) can be used.

Cognitive Dysfunction Protracted withdrawal can interfere with the addict's processing of treatment information, suggesting that treatment should not rely too heavily on psychoeducational approaches. A careful assessment can prevent excessive therapeutic expectations. Protracted withdrawal can also create much subjective distress and dilute the benefits of early recovery. Many alcoholics begin to feel so ill at ease when they are not drinking

Table 5.2. Assessment Instruments for Various Addictions

Addiction	Name of Instrument	Type of Instrument	Reference
Alcoholism	Alcohol Use Inventory	Self-Report	Horn, Wanberg, & Foster (1987)
	MacAndrew Alcoholism Scale	Self-Report	MacAndrew (1965)
	Alcohol Dependence Scale	Self-Report	Skinner & Horn (1984)
	Comprehensive Drinker Profile	Interview	Marlatt & Miller (1984)
	Michigan Alcoholism Screening Test	Self-Report	Selzer (1971)
Drug Addiction	Addiction Severity Index	Interview	McLellan, Luborsky, Woody, & O'Brien (1980)
	Cocaine Abuse Assessment Profile	Self-Report	Washton, Stone, & Hendrickson (1988)
	Drug Abuse Screening Test	Self-Report	Skinner (1982)
Nicotine Addiction	Tolerance Questionnaire	Self-Report	Fagerstrom (1978)
	Schiffman-Jarvik Withdrawal Scale	Self-Report	Schiffman & Jarvik (1976)
	Reasons for Smoking Scale	Self-Report	Ikard, Green, & Horn (1969)
Eating Disorders	Eating Attitudes Test	Self-Report	Garner & Garfinkel (1979)
	Eating Disorder Inventory	Self-Report	Garner & Olmstead (1984)
	Diagnostic Survey for Eating Disorders	Interview	Johnson (1985)
Compulsive Gambling	South Oaks Gambling Screen	Self-Report	Blume & Lesieur (1988)

that they conclude drinking made them feel more comfortable. Such assumptions can lead to relapse unless the recovering person is forewarned and taught cognitive remediation techniques (see chapter 6).

Assessment of protracted withdrawal can be achieved through three methods: (a) neuropsychological testing, (b) psychiatric and psychological questionnaires, and (c) observation and self-monitoring. These methods can be administered periodically to assess the return to the client of cognitive function, as most of the recovery will occur in the first few months of abstinence.

Neuropsychological testing should focus on short-term memory, abstract reasoning, and problem solving. Memory tests should evaluate stimuli that are familiar and unfamiliar, recent and immediate, and visual and auditory. The Wechsler Adult Intelligence Scale-Revised (Wechsler, 1981) can be used to screen all of these functions. The Wechsler Memory Scale (Wechsler, 1945) taps various dimensions of visual and verbal memory. Miller and Saucedo (1983) reviewed results of these tests among alcoholics and found that short-term memory, encoding, and retrieval problems are fairly common in early recovery. Intelligence test results suggest that alcoholics score within the average range of intelligence and have normal vocabulary levels. They perform more poorly on attentional and visual-spatial tasks.

Abstract reasoning tests should focus on both verbal and nonverbal concept formation. The abstraction portion of the Shipley Institute of Living Scale (Shipley, 1967) and Category Test of the Halstead-Reitan Battery (Halstead, 1947) provide measures of nonverbal and verbal abstract reasoning, respectively. Miller and Saucedo (1983) reported that abstract reasoning is found to be impaired among alcoholics in about half of the studies.

Problem-solving tests should focus on the patient's ability both to generate solutions and to shift response set. The Trailmaking Test (Army Individual Test, 1944) requires patients to draw lines connecting numbers and letters in an alternating sequence. The Wisconsin Card Sort (Grant & Berg, 1948) requires patients to develop problem-solving strategies to sort cards with designs of different shapes and colors. Miller and Saucedo (1983) found that alcoholics tend to perseverate with incorrect strategies and have problems retaining a correct strategy (i.e., they commit errors even after determining the correct answer). These cognitive difficulties have ramifications for an addicted person's ability to solve problems in early recovery.

For further details about these and other instruments, the reader is referred to Miller and Saucedo (1983) or Berg, Franzen, and Wedding (1987). These authors recommend multidimensional assessments, since no single neuropsychological test will provide definitive information.

Psychiatric and psychological questionnaires provide useful information because protracted withdrawal symptoms often mimic psychiatric symptoms. Repeated evaluations typically reveal a decrease in these symptoms in most patients. For a broad range of symptoms, the Symptom Checklist 90 (SCL-90-R) developed by Derogatis (1977) has been shown to be informative (DeSoto, O'Donnell, Allred, & Lopes, 1985). The MMPI can reflect psychological changes that occur over a period of abstinence (Pettinati, Sugerman, & Maurer, 1982). The mood disorders secondary to withdrawal can be monitored with the Beck Depression Inventory (Beck,

Ward, Mendelson, Mock, & Erbaugh, 1961), which often shows changes within the first month of treatment.

Observation and self-monitoring allow a more individualized approach to assessment of cognitive dysfunction. Observation or questioning about sleep patterns, memory, recall of simple information such as names, schedules, and telephone numbers, and emotional lability yields good naturalistic information about protracted withdrawal. Patients may also complain of "foggy" thinking, blocking in the middle of conversations, difficulties reading without several repetitions, and emotional flatness. McCrady (1987, p. 387) suggests that the following recovery-related skills may be impaired by neuropsychological effects:

- the ability to remember information presented in treatment
- the ability to remember why drinking is a problem and abstinence is necessary
- the ability to find treatment, A.A. meetings, or even one's way around the treatment facility
- the ability to associate names with faces in A.A. or group therapy meetings
- the ability to listen to discussions and glean relevant information from individual and group therapy
- the ability to identify high risk situations
- the ability to generate solutions to problems resulting from or independent of drinking
- lack of problem-solving skills, that is, the ability to select possible solutions, try them out, evaluate their effectiveness, and alter unsuccessful solutions
- the ability to carry on conversations
- the ability to recognize the consequences of continued drinking

Some researchers have even used quizzes of treatment-relevant information to assess patients' memory (Becker & Jaffe, 1984). During early phases of treatment, patients may not be able to extract *any* important information, but this tends to improve with time. This finding is extremely important because we expect patients to recall information when they leave treatment. Ongoing assessment of how well patients recall treatment information may therefore enhance their compliance and the outcome of therapy.

Craving and Cue Reactivity The strength of cue reactivity is frequently underestimated by clinicians and patients, particularly in the safety of inpatient settings. Because few patients realize the assortment of emotional, interpersonal, and environmental stimuli that can trigger craving, clinicians need to approach the assessment of these cues in a comprehensive manner.

Cue reactivity can be assessed by three methods: (a) rating scales, (b) imagery, or (c) exposure. Among the rating scales, the Inventory of Drinking Situations, developed by Annis, Graham, and Davis (1987), includes an "Urges and Temptations to Drink" section among its seven scales. This portion includes items such as "I drank heavily when I passed by a liquor store" or "I drank heavily when I remembered how good it tasted." The score on this scale can be calculated in relation to other types of interpersonal and intrapersonal triggers.

The clinician can also construct a list of relevant and individualized cues with the patient. The patient can rate each of these cues for relapse potential and keep an ongoing record of ratings throughout treatment. A list of potential craving cues is presented in Table 5.3.

Imagery provides another useful avenue of assessment. Clinicians can use structured interview information and patient ratings of craving cues (1 = no craving, 5 = intense craving) to construct a vivid, individualized, and realistic scenario for each patient. The patient is then asked to imagine the situation, which focuses on his or her behaviors and thoughts when faced with the drinking cues. These scenarios are approximately 2 to 3 minutes in length. The patient rates the intensity of each scenario on the 1 to 5 scale devised to measure craving. Behavioral signs such as squirming, sweating, or flushing should also be monitored. The following is a sample scenario:

> You have worked a long hard day and have been thinking about drinking the whole time. You begin to feel edgy and impatient as your boss gives you

Table 5.3. Common Triggers for Craving

Television or movie scenes with substance use
Cigarette rolling papers
Razor blades
Hypodermic needles
Plastic bags
Beer advertisements on television
Music videos
Photographs of parties with drinking or drug use
The sound of a "pop top" opener on a beer can
Music with drug or drinking lyrics
Music listened to while drinking or using drugs
The smell of liquor
The smell of marijuana
The smell of benzene (often used to process cocaine)
Getting a paycheck
Certain times of the day or week
Activities related to substance use (watching television, smoking cigarettes, playing cards)
T-shirts with drug or alcohol slogans
Driver's license or credit card (for cutting cocaine)
Soda bottle (for smoking cocaine)
White powdery substances (baking soda, baby powder, salt)

your check. You rush to your car and can't help but think about how good that first beer is going to taste. You are sweaty and your mouth is dry. As you drive down the street, you see your favorite package store. You pull the car into a parking space and rush in. You take two six-packs of beer out of the cooler and pay the cashier. You return to your car, but you can't wait any longer. You grab one of the frosty, cool beers, which by now has drops of water on the outside. You pop it open . . . WHHIISSHH . . . and immediately smell the beer as the foam peeks out of the top. You swallow the first sip and it cools your throat as it travels down. It tastes wonderful and all your edginess begins to go away. You take in the next sip and start to relax from all of the day's troubles.

Rimmele, Miller, and Dougher (1989) provide a more detailed description of "covert sensitization," which requires a later pairing with an avoidance response. Patients should not be exposed to such cues without also learning coping skills that help them compensate for craving. Exposure in the absence of coping skills can decrease self-efficacy. These skills include relaxation, assertiveness, cognitive restructuring, and/or stimulus control. They are reviewed in chapter 6.

Actual exposure to objects, situations, or places provides the most realistic indication of a person's ability to cope with craving cues. Rather than using alcohol or drugs themselves, it is relatively easy to find objects (particularly with cocaine addicts) that are strongly associated with alcohol or drug use. In fact, even in inpatient settings, many patients are reminded of substance use by seemingly innocuous objects. These can include soda bottles (cocaine freebasing), artificial sweetener, tin foil (cocaine freebasing), drivers' licenses (for cutting up cocaine), or plastic bags (for storing drugs). Playing particular songs, having another patient tell a "war story" (highlighting the positive aspects of drug use), and showing a movie scene that contains drug use are other methods of gauging reactions to cues. Additional items may be drawn from Table 5.3. The same rating scale should be used for measuring reaction to all items. *It is critical to teach the patient coping responses if any type of exposure is used.*

Sensation Seeking Addicts and alcoholics often use substances in an attempt to maintain an optimal level of stimulation. Those who find the world too stimulating may consume tranquilizing or sedative drugs. Those who find it boring and tedious may turn to drugs with stimulant properties. It is difficult to measure this optimal level beyond a self-report, but patients can usually identify the direction in which they like drugs to take them. I often ask, "If the world were a radio, would you be turning the volume up or down?" Stimulant users usually like the "volume" up, while depressant users like it down.

Sensation seeking can also be measured with Zuckerman's (1979) Sensation Seeking Scale. This scale measures four different aspects of sensation seeking: (a) Thrill and Adventure Seeking (the desire to try risky activities involving speed, height, or movement, such as driving fast); (b) Experience Seeking (the desire to seek experiences through the mind and senses, such as art or travel); (c) Disinhibition (the desire for extroverted and uninhibited activities, such as parties or multiple sexual partners); and (d) Boredom Susceptibility (an aversion to monotony and predictability). Those who are sensation seekers may have difficulty with the routine and greater predictability of a life without drugs or alcohol. High scores on these scales suggest the need to determine new and healthy stimulating activities or to help the patient modulate his optimal level of stimulation (e.g., through relaxation training).

Physical Health Factors The patient's ability to cope with physical problems needs to be assessed because mismanagement of physical problems is a common precursor to relapse. The same denial process that operates with addictions is present in physical disorders; this will often give clues about the patient's commitment to recovery from addictive disorders. A tendency to somatize may indicate that the patient does not readily identify emotions or troublesome situations that might lead to relapse. Finally, many people relapse after being given medication for pain or injuries. Preparation for dealing with doctors, hospitals, and treatments can often prevent relapse. Patients should be reminded to avoid unnecessary visits to doctors and dentists, to detail their alcohol and drug histories honestly when they do require treatment, and to get complete information about *any* medication that they are receiving. In addition, patients can call doctors, state their problem, and have it recorded before their visit.

Psychological Risk Analysis

Expectancy Expectancies about one's preferred substance, treatment, self-help, relapse, and recovery can combine to produce powerful effects on outcome. Many individuals seek particular desirable effects in substance use, although not necessarily on every occasion. The degree to which nondrug activities can create similar desirable conditions may provide insights into potential healthy replacements for drug use. Conversely, the negative effects may need to be emphasized to decrease urges to use alcohol or drugs. This is reminiscent of A.A. advice to "think through the drink." Keep in mind that age, length of abstinence, population (drunken drivers, college students, adolescents), and even beverage type (hard liquor vs. beer vs. drugs) can affect these expectancies (Leigh, 1989).

Several questionnaires can measure such expectancies, the most frequently used being the Alcohol Expectancy Questionnaire (Brown, Goldman, Inn, & Anderson, 1980). Respondents indicate whether they agree or disagree with particular effects of alcohol use (e.g., "Alcohol increases aggressiveness," "Drinking makes me feel flushed," "Alcohol makes me feel happy," "Alcohol seems like magic"). Southwick, Steele, Marlatt, and Lindell (1981) devised the Alcohol Effects Scale, which requires respondents to rate effects along a 5-point bipolar scale (e.g., happy/sad, tense/relaxed, clumsy/coordinated). Leigh (1987) developed the Effects of Drinking Alcohol questionnaire to tap the strength with which respondents hold certain beliefs about alcohol. Items such as "feel sleepy," "become friendly," and "feel depressed" are rated on scales from 1 to 5 (1 = unlikely, 5 = likely). Measuring expectancy can be complex. The reader is therefore referred to Leigh's (1989b) review of assessment of expectancy which provides more detail about the reliability and validity of these questionnaires.

There are no scales to measure expectancies about addiction treatment and recovery, but this information can be obtained by assessing the patient's knowledge of relapse. Presenting "relapse mythology" (see chapter 2) in the form of a true-false quiz can often reveal patients' misconceptions about recovery, even among those who have had significant involvement in treatment and A.A. Many of these misconceptions arise *because* of incorrect information presented in treatment or through A.A. Clinicians can correct misconceptions by reviewing the results of the quiz and providing appropriate educational literature. Gorski and Miller (1987) have written a booklet entitled "Mistaken Beliefs About Relapse" that offers a review of relapse myths from an A.A. and alcohol counseling viewpoint.

Coping Skills Coping skills comprise a range of intrapersonal and interpersonal behavior. These skills include social skills, problem solving, emotional management, and cognitive coping. The presence of deficiencies in any of these areas will guide the treatment strategy.

Situations relevant to all these skills can be evaluated by first obtaining an individualized list of high risk situations from each patient. The Inventory of Drinking Situations (Annis, 1982) discussed earlier delineates a variety of interpersonal and intrapersonal high risk situations. The seven scales include intrapersonal situations (unpleasant emotions, physical discomfort, pleasant emotions, testing personal control, and urges and temptations) and interpersonal situations (conflict with others, social pressure to drink, and pleasant times with others). The Relapse Precipitants Inventory, a 25-item questionnaire developed by Litman, Stapleton, Oppenheim, Peleg, and Jackson (1983), provides similar classes of items. Patients can then provide self-efficacy information for these situations by rating their confidence levels in the Situational Confidence Questionnaire (Annis, 1987).

The assessment can be refined by determining patterns of risk that provide clues about client vulnerability. If there is an undifferentiated pattern (similar scores yielding a flat pattern), the client tends to see risk in most situations. If there is a differentiated pattern (elevations on particular scales), the risk is variable and more identifiable. Presumably, the latter should be easier to target for intervention.

In addition, the similarity of the Inventory of Drinking Situations and the Situational Confidence Questionnaire allows comparison of the relative risk and confidence level for each type of situation. For instance, if an alcoholic reported high risk but low self-efficacy with "urges and temptations," this situation would be more likely to lead to a relapse than if it had a combination of high risk and high self-efficacy. Risk and self-efficacy should be determined for each significant situation.

When faced with high risk, the individual is required to identify and develop solutions for problems. Problem solving can be measured directly through the Ways of Coping Questionnaire (WCQ) (Folkman & Lazarus, 1988) and the Coping Resources Inventory (CRI) (Hammer & Marting, 1987). With these questionnaires the clinician can target deficient coping skills or resources. The WCQ measures coping *processes* that people use in response to stressful encounters of daily living. The eight scales and respective sample items from the WCQ are listed in Table 5.4.

The CRI measures personal *resources* for coping with stress. The six scales of the CRI and sample items from each are listed in Table 5.5.

Life events in early recovery (especially when combined with cognitive dysfunction) frequently tax patients' problem-solving abilities. Patients should therefore be questioned about any possible family, social, personal, and employment changes. These can be assessed with the Social Readjustment Rating Scale (Holmes & Rahe, 1967). Physical illness has been associated with 80% of those who score greater than 300 on this scale. Because this instrument is geared for physical illness, patients should be asked about the relationship between any high-probability items and substance use.

Emotional management is particularly challenging in early recovery. Many alcoholics and addicts relapse due to emotional *mismanagement* (Marlatt, 1985a). Anger, guilt, loneliness, and sadness are probably the most difficult emotions to handle, but positive emotions can often be just as demanding. Euphoria (the "pink cloud") and complacency are also quite frequent. Not all recovering alcoholics and addicts meet the criteria for psychiatric diagnoses, but all feel emotional disruption. Questioning patients about how they identify these feelings in their bodily reactions, thoughts, and behaviors may help unearth potential high-risk emotional states. The appropriateness of emotions to particular situations should also be evaluated. For instance, does the patient laugh in response to serious situations or cry in response to happy situations? Does he or she feel a

Table 5.4. Sample Items from the "Ways of Coping Questionnaire"

Confrontative Coping
    28. I let my feelings out somehow.
    34. Took a big chance or did something very risky.
Distancing
    13. Went on as if nothing had happened.
    21. Tried to forget the whole thing.
Self-Controlling
    14. I tried to keep my feelings to myself.
    62. I went over in my mind what I would say or do.
Seeking Social Support
    18. Accepted sympathy and understanding from someone.
    22. I got professional help.
Accepting Responsibility
    9. Criticized and lectured myself.
    29. Realized I brought the problem on myself.
Escape–Avoidance
    11. Hoped a miracle would happen.
    47. Took it out on other people.
Planful Problem Solving
    26. I made a plan of action and followed it.
    48. Drew on my past experiences; I was in a similar position
        before.
Positive Reappraisal
    38. Rediscovered what is important in life.
    60. I prayed.

Note: Reproduced by special permission of the Publisher, Consulting Psychologists Press, Inc., Palo Alto, CA 94306, from the Ways of Coping Questionnaire by Susan Folkman & Richard Lazarus © 1988. Further reproduction is prohibited without the Publisher's consent.

Table 5.5. Sample Items from the "Coping Resources Inventory"

Cognitive
    6. I feel as worthwhile as anyone else.
    18. I am aware of my good qualities.
Social
    9. I am part of a group, other than my family, that cares about me.
    35. I enjoy being with other people.
Emotional
    29. I can cry when sad.
    39. I express my feelings of joy.
Spiritual and Philosophical
    33. I know what is important in life.
    52. I take time to reflect on my life.
Physical
    42. I do stretching exercises.
    60. I am in good physical shape.

Note: Reproduced by special permission of the Publisher, Consulting Psychologists Press, Inc., Palo Alto, CA 94306, from Coping Resources Inventory by Allen L. Hammer & M. Susan Marting © 1987. Further reproduction is prohibited without the Publisher's consent.

right to express emotions? What messages about expressing emotions were given by the family of origin?

It is also necessary to assess how alcoholics and addicts think themselves through a problem and what they say to themselves. This can be accomplished through use of the "thought listing" technique described by Cacioppo and Petty (1981). The patient is presented with a hypothetical high-risk situation or asked to recall spontaneous thoughts that occurred while he or she was anticipating or attending to a real-life situation. The patient provides spoken or written commentary. The clinician can then review the effectiveness of these thoughts and provide appropriate alternatives.

Some of these thoughts are repetitive and automatic. I have used a "Famous Quotes" exercise in which patients generate well-worn statements that they make to themselves under trying conditions. Since many of these statements are also made aloud, it may also be useful to request examples of these quotes from significant others. Patients can then be asked to self-monitor these statements as treatment progresses.

"Seemingly irrelevant decisions" (SIDs) (Monti et al., 1989), or as they were originally called, "apparently irrelevant decisions" (Marlatt & Gordon, 1985), refer to the conscious and unconscious decisions that alcoholics and addicts make on the way to a relapse. The risk of these decisions is underestimated and the individual "sets up" a relapse. Rather than accepting excuses such as "I found myself with a drink in my hand," clinicians should trace the sequence of events leading to the relapse. These are some of the classic SIDs:

1. drinking soda in a bar while friends are drinking alcohol
2. using the "marijuana maintenance program," that is, substituting one drug for another
3. drinking nonalcoholic beer (which often results in drunk-like behavior)
4. driving past the old drinking haunts
5. making excuses to visit a drug dealer, for example, "I owe him money"

Cognitive coping is also affected by one's definitions of *lapse* and *relapse.* The distinction between them is quite subjective, but it is meaningful in terms of what attributions patients make about their substance use. If *any* usage means that one has lost control, continued usage is highly likely. The "abstinence violation effect" (Marlatt & Gordon, 1985), which is an intense feeling of guilt and failure in response to a lapse, predominates. Patients' definition of, perception of, and response to lapses is critical in determining their ability to reverse the course to relapse. Do they see a lapse as a mistake or a failure? Do they become guilty or remotivated? Do they assume that they lost control and give up or do they learn from their mistake? For each person, how long does it take to turn a lapse into a relapse?

Personality DSM-III-R Axis II diagnoses often go undetected because of the complexity of symptoms presented by alcoholics and addicts. Dual diagnoses are usually reserved for those with Axis I conditions. However, the presence of an Axis II disorder can often provide information that is predictive not only of the likelihood of relapse but also of how it will transpire.

Shapiro's (1965) analysis of neurotic styles, although not directed at substance abuse, is particularly instructive. He describes the obsessive-compulsive, paranoid, hysterical, and impulsive styles. The obsessive-compulsive types are rigid, overcontrolled, persistent even in the face of failure, lacking in spontaneity, and task oriented. These people have difficulty in recovery because they lack flexibility for change and because they focus on tasks rather than feelings. Paranoid types are hypervigilant, suspicious, negative, and biased. They lack the openmindedness to address the consequences of their addictions. The hysterical types are unfocused, uninsightful, impressionistic, and repressing. They have difficulty in recovery because of their inability to understand the connection between their addictive behavior and their poor adjustment. The impulsive ones are characterized by poor planning, blaming of others, low frustration tolerance, and difficulty integrating feedback. In recovery, these individuals are likely to set their own course, break rules, and deny their addictions. All of these styles experience impaired relationships.

This approach can be applied to current Axis II categories. Table 5.6 describes the possible definitions of recovery, views of help seeking, interpersonal relations, and relapse predictors for each personality disorder.

Psychopathology A complete discussion of psychopathology and substance abuse is beyond the scope of this chapter, but several suggestions can be made about assessment in relation to relapse potential. First, it is difficult to determine psychopathological factors while the patient is in withdrawal. If a therapist waits a minimum of 2 to 3 weeks before diagnosing a psychiatric problem he or she will achieve a more reliable diagnosis.

Second, psychological testing completed at early phases of recovery will often produce false positives or false negatives. Tests such as the Structured Clinical Interview for DSM-III-R (Spitzer, Williams, Gibbon & First, 1990), the Minnesota Multiphasic Personality Inventory (MMPI-2), and the Millon Clinical Multiaxial Inventory (MCMI-2) are extremely useful but only after the emotional and physical upheaval of withdrawal have settled.

Third, I have found it useful to review neuropsychological and personality test results not only to reinforce the negative effects of substance use

Table 5.6. Personality Disorders and Behaviors in Recovery

Personality Disorders	Self-Reported Key to Recovery	Help Seeking Pattern	Risk Factors
Paranoid	Willpower and Lack of Provocation from Others	Avoid due to Lack of Trust	Angry; Isolative; Negative
Dependent	Having a Stable Relationship	Too Reliant on Others	Indecisive; Passive; Lack of Self-Confidence
Avoidant	Being Accepted by Others	Avoid due to Fear of Rejection	Isolative; Anxious; No Feedback
Passive-Aggressive	Compliance with Suggestions (Superficial)	Tend to Rely on Themselves due to Mistrust of Others	Angry; Dishonest; Superficial
Compulsive	Organization and Predictability in Life	Rely on Themselves due to Need to Feel Competent	Overcontrol; Too much Work; Rigidity; Stress
Antisocial	Staying out of Trouble and Using Willpower	Avoid due to Dislike of Structure and Expectations	"My Way"; Disorganized; Angry; In Conflict
Borderline	Living a Stable Life Without Destructive Relationships	Fluctuate Between lack of or too much Involvement	Disorganized; Acting out; Conflict
Narcissistic	Willpower	Often Do not Understand Need for Help	Overconfident; Unprepared; Superficial
Schizoid	Willpower and Lack of Interference from Others	Do not See the Need to Involve Others in Recovery	Isolative; Detached; Negative; Angry

but also to get the patient's impressions of which findings relate to substance effects versus underlying psychopathology.

Fourth, the *dynamics* of (not just the side effects caused by) medication taking need to be considered carefully. The act of medication taking can (a) act as cue exposure, (b) reintroduce a patient into the medical system (where he may have manipulated doctors for medication), and (3) place patients in a dependent stance where they expect immediate solutions to emotional issues. Patient attitudes and expectations about medication need to be assessed.

Fifth, the possibility of posttraumatic stress disorder, particularly in response to sexual abuse, should be examined. Because of the high incidence of physical and sexual abuse in alcoholic families, many children of alcoholics and addicts experience depression, anxiety, relationship problems, compulsive tendencies, and, of course, substance abuse of their own (Young, 1990). Approximately 75% of substance-dependent women in inpatient settings report childhood sexual abuse (Rohsenow, Corbett, & Devine, 1988). Early sexual abuse may predispose women to develop alcoholism (Covington, 1986). The incidence of sexual abuse among males, many of whom become alcoholic, is also beginning to gain recognition (Lew, 1988).

Victims of sexual abuse may lose sight of the original stressors and experience an awakening of these symptoms as their emotions and memories become clearer. The resulting confusion can trigger events leading to relapse. The clinician is well advised to ask specifically about any incidents of incest, molestation, physical abuse, verbal abuse, or other severe stressors during developmental years. Although few recovering people are equipped to address such trauma early in recovery, they can at least begin to understand the sources of their unhealthy behavior. Table 5.7 lists behavioral signs that should alert the clinician to evaluate the possibility of sexual abuse.

Finally, there is a need to explore the relationship between past substance use and psychopathology. Was it an additive effect where an underlying psychiatric problem was expressed only when substances were used? Did continual substance usage produce psychiatric effects? Did the patient

Table 5.7. Symptoms of Sexual Abuse

- Inability to remember large portions of childhood
- Extreme sexual behavior, such as engaging in compulsive sexual activity or avoiding sex entirely
- Nightmares, flashbacks, or fear of going to bed, bathing, or taking a shower
- Inability to express feelings
- Sharp startle response or fear of being touched
- Tendency to enter into destructive relationships
- Feelings of isolation from people
- Inexplicable aversion to certain family members
- Feelings of worthlessness, self-hatred, or low self-esteem
- Feelings of disgust about one's body
- Difficulty forming and maintaining relationships
- Inexplicable feelings of shame or guilt
- Recurring depression

Note: Adapted from Lew (1988)

self-medicate an underlying psychiatric problem? All of these questions have different implications for relapse prevention (discussed in chapter 6).

Social Risk Analysis

Relationship Stability Relationship instability can arise from ongoing conflicts, substance abuse or psychiatric problems in significant others, a lack of understanding about addiction, poor communication skills, or psychosocial stress. The conflicts may relate to substance abuse or dysfunction in the relationship; the clinician should assess the degree to which relationships are impaired simply because of substance use. Difficulties in problem solving, open discussion of emotions, philosophies of child rearing and discipline, or sexual function are frequently intertwined with the effects of drugs and alcohol.

Substance abuse and psychiatric problems in significant others is a particularly thorny problem. These problems may create a lack of emotional availability that interferes with the development of social support. The feedback needed in early recovery may therefore be absent or inaccurate. To develop healthy feedback within the family, the significant other may need education about obtaining his or her own substance abuse or psychiatric treatment. To address this issue several key questions should be asked of the people in the support role: (a) Do they feel that they have been affected by substance abuse in the family? (b) Do they see a need for help for themselves? (c) Are they willing to make a commitment to counseling or Al-Anon? (d) Do they have social or therapeutic support for themselves while the patient is attending to his own recovery?

Alcoholics and addicts often lack communication skills in family, social, and intimate relationships. Are the rules and expectations of the relationship clearly stated? How are problems solved, if at all? Can the communication style be regarded as assertive, aggressive, passive, or passive-aggressive? Are resentments addressed openly? Are differing opinions tolerated? How much independence can be supported? All these questions have meaning for the future of the relationships, the potency of treatment, and the potential for relapse.

Psychosocial stress can upset coping abilities in a relationship. Relationships already stressed by substance use can lose even more resilience when life events occur. Is anyone in the family ill? Has anyone recently died? Have there been any major losses? How does the family cope with such events? Have there been residential, financial, employment, or social changes that affect the whole family? To what extent is the family able to address the life event and still commit itself to recovery?

Moos and Moos (1986) developed the Family Environment Scale to measure the social climate and resources of family systems. This scale assesses the quality of family relationships, issues of personal growth, and family ability to change. Clinicians can use this scale to target deficiencies that might contribute to relapse. Table 5.8 displays the subscales with representative items.

Work relationships can be negative or positive influences in the addicted person's life because they can either (a) increase relapse risk through stress or exposure to addicting substances or (b) constitute the only available drug-free interpersonal contacts. Work serves an organizing function in the life of a substance abuser because he or she needs work to get money for drugs. If work also becomes a place to use substances, the probability of relapse increases dramatically. As in the family, the quality of communication, the problem-solving style, and degree of stress in the work place can affect relapse potential. Moos (1986) developed the Work Environment

Table 5.8. Sample Items from the "Family Environment Scale"

Cohesion
   1. Family members really help and support one another.
   11. We often seem to be killing time at home.
Expressiveness
   12. We say anything we want to around home.
   32. We tell each other about our personal problems.
Conflict
   3. We fight a lot in our family.
   13. Family members rarely become openly angry.
Independence
   24. We think things out for ourselves in our family.
   34. We come and go as we want in our family.
Achievement Orientation
   15. Getting ahead in life is very important in our family.
   35. We believe in competition and "may the best man win."
Intellectual-Cultural Orientation
   6. We often talk about political and social problems.
   16. We rarely go to lectures, plays, or concerts.
Active-Recreational Orientation
   7. We spend most evenings and weekends at home.
   17. Friends often come over for dinner or to visit.
Moral-Religious Emphasis
   18. We do not say any prayers in our family.
   38. We do not believe in heaven or hell.
Organization
   9. Activities in my family are pretty carefully planned.
   19. We are generally very neat and orderly.
Control
   10. Family members are rarely ordered around.
   20. There are very few rules to follow in our family.

Scale to assess work commitment, work style, and emphasis on rules and policies. This scale can be used to locate potential relapse precipitants in the work environment.

Environmental Stability Environmental stability is a broad term comprising physical living arrangements, types of neighborhoods, proximity to drinking and drug environments, and the consistency of living arrangements. Cramped, uncomfortable, crowded, or unhealthy living quarters can increase stress and conflict. Neighborhoods that are dangerous or rampant with drug dealing may actively interfere with recovery. Close proximity to drinking or drug environments will increase cue exposure. Inconsistent living arrangements will dilute social support and encourage transitory relationships. In such environments, the recovering individual may have to develop alternative traveling routes in order to minimize risk. At the same time, clinicians need to caution against "geographical cures," which are environmental changes made to escape responsibility.

Relapse Workbooks

Patients can take a more active role in the assessment process by completing relapse workbooks. Gorski (1988) and Daley (1986) have written workbooks aimed at an adult substance abusing population and Chiauzzi and Liljegren (1990) have produced one for adolescent substance abusers. Rustin (1989) has adapted relapse prevention principles for cigarette smoking. The following are highlights of each workbook.

The Relapse Prevention Workbook Daley's (1986) workbook on relapse prevention is aimed at patients in treatment for the first time or after a relapse. It is completed by the patient and and reviewed with the clinician. Through a series of writing assignments highlighting the high-risk factors that precede relapse, patients can become aware of trouble spots in their recoveries. Respondents are asked to assess their negative feelings, social pressures, treatment-related problems, difficulties in relationships, and craving. They use this information to develop strategies for handling anger, using leisure time, and responding to emergencies. Since relapse prevention is an ongoing process, respondents are also encouraged to maintain a relapse prevention inventory that monitors warning signs on a daily basis. The problem-solving focus of this workbook is useful in assisting patients to monitor risk through early recovery.

The Staying Sober Workbook Gorski's (1988) workbook is based on the relapse prevention model developed by Gorski and Miller (1986). Patients attempting to stay sober are guided through the recovery steps of stabilization, self-assessment, relapse education, warning sign identification, warning sign management, inventory training, involvement of significant others, and follow-up. Postacute withdrawal, relapse history, treatment need, and adherence to the steps outlined by A.A. are also highlighted. Patients learn about their recoveries through completion of checklists, self-monitoring, or development of lists of significant risk factors. Patients are encouraged to develop a relapse prevention network, which is a group of people who support recovery.

Staying Straight: A Relapse Prevention Workbook for Young People The workbook by Chiauzzi and Liljegren (1990) is geared toward adolescents in treatment and requires them to seek assistance from "straight" adults or peers in recovery. It is interactive, as the adolescent cannot complete the workbook without seeking outside assistance or sharing new insights with counselors, parents, teachers, or friends. The workbook is based on the biopsychosocial model presented in this book. In three sections entitled "What Do You Know About Relapse?", "What Do You Know About Yourself?", and "What You Need To Stay Straight", tasks are divided into biological, psychological, and social self-assessments and tasks. Biological tasks focus on craving management, psychological tasks focus on feelings and behaviors that lead to relapse, and social tasks focus on assessment of friendships and development of healthful activities. Respondents are encouraged to complete a relapse contract with a significant other and to construct "straight cards" with lists of "safe" people. These activities build an emergency plan into recovery in the event that the adolescent lapses or becomes involved in a high risk situation.

Quit and Stay Quit Rustin's (1989) workbook is a medical treatment program for smokers. It is meant for individuals who are actively being treated in group settings with trained group facilitators. It is not meant as a self-help workbook. Rustin adapts relapse prevention and 12-step principles to nicotine addiction. He includes exercises requiring respondents to assess their motivations, explore their feelings, examine their attitudes about smoking, develop strategies such as relaxation, "make amends" to others, devise a relapse plan, and monitor relapse behaviors on a daily basis. This workbook provides useful information about nicotine addiction, with emphasis on biological, psychological, and social relapse prevention.

SUMMARY

This chapter provided a framework for assessing historical, biological, psychological, and social risk factors. By applying available behavioral interviewing and assessment techniques to individual problem areas, the clinician can develop a profile of risk factors that can guide treatment. The next chapter reviews interventions for each risk factor.

Chapter 6

Relapse Prevention Techniques

Assume a virtue if you have it not
. . . and refrain tonight;
And that shall lend a kind of easiness
To the next abstinence: the next more easy;
For use almost can change the stamp of nature
And master ev'n the devil or throw him out
With wondrous potency.
　　　　　—Shakespeare (Hamlet, Act III, Scene 4)

All effective substance abuse treatments have one common feature: They keep the addicted person away from risk factors that precipitate drug use. The biopsychosocial viewpoint implies that interventions to prevent relapse will conform to the most critical factors identified in the assessment process. For treatment truly to be individualized, a careful balance of biological, psychological, and social factors must be determined. This orientation will avoid the pitfalls of traditional treatment, which focuses heavily on the biological ("disease") component without addressing psychological and social components. With this method the patient has greater control over the latter two domains.

This chapter addresses cognitive-behavioral interventions for biological, psychological, and social components of addiction. Since all addiction treatment can be considered relapse prevention, the intent of this chapter is to provide an organizational framework for these interventions. For further details about the sources of specific techniques, please refer to Appendix B.

THERAPIST ORIENTATION—IS IT IMPORTANT?

One of the most enduring beliefs among counselors and patients alike is that counselors and therapists should be recovering alcoholics or addicts to be effective. Patients often ask, "How can you understand if you've never been there?" Many counselors rely on their experiences in recovery to guide their patients through early recovery. In contrast to other mental health treatments, a patient in one's caseload one day can become a peer in an Alcoholics Anonymous meeting the next. The bond that develops between counselors and their patients can often be therapeutic, but it may encourage an exclusive reliance on A.A. as a therapeutic intervention. As stated throughout this book, reliance on any one viewpoint creates an unnecessarily rigid and counterproductive approach to treatment (which ultimately can increase the risk of relapse). Counselors then lack knowledge about potentially effective techniques from other disciplines.

On the other hand, a repudiation of the importance (and reality) of self-help can be equally counterproductive. Therapists outside the recovering community have consistently underestimated the multiplicity of viewpoints among Alcoholics Anonymous members. The pronouncements of disease model advocates seem unbending, but my conversations with A.A. members lead me to believe that this is a pragmatic group of people. Among younger members, who have grown up with a greater awareness of mental health approaches, there seems to be a recognition that "some people need more than A.A."

The therapist who can skillfully guide a patient to develop a personally meaningful formula that builds social support with self-change will ultimately achieve the most success. The issue of the therapist's involvement in recovery (or lack thereof) will be an issue only if the patient is (a) not focusing on treatment, but on extraneous concerns; (b) trying to determine whether the therapist is qualified and knowledgeable in the addictions; or (c) struggling with trust issues. The therapist should not attempt to prove his or her competence or knowledge to an addict or alcoholic. There is also no need for the nonrecovering therapist to act as a quasi-A.A. member. Alcoholics and addicts tend to be skeptical people who can be difficult to please. Instead, the therapist should allay the patient's concerns about his or her ability to help by providing a specific and carefully considered treatment strategy. Goals should be mutually established and the rationale for all interventions should be explained. Any therapist, recovering or not, will be perceived as rigid and uncaring if he or she does not recognize the importance of the patient's perceptions of treatment.

INCREASING MOTIVATION

In order to deliver treatment effectively, it is important that the therapist develop a cooperative, creative, and optimistic atmosphere for change. Negotiation, rather than confrontation, should be the primary therapeutic stance. Based on research on effective techniques, Miller (1989) suggests eight motivational interventions that are related to positive outcome:

1. *A*dvice—offer minimal advice, which sometimes motivates change.
2. *B*arriers—remove barriers to change, for example, child care for women or the distance that the patient needs to travel for treatment.
3. *C*hoice—provide alternatives instead of limiting the addicted person's options.
4. *D*ecrease attractiveness—make the alcoholic aware of negative consequences of drinking or drug use.
5. *E*xternal contingencies—if using coercion, make the contingency firm and indefinite.
6. *F*eedback—provide individualized feedback, since general feedback in the form of alcohol or drug education is of questionable usefulness.
7. *G*oal-setting—clarify and negotiate, rather than prescribe, goals.
8. *H*elping attitude—display empathy and optimism, which are related to a favorable outcome.

When applying interventions, this ABCDEFGH model should be the foundation. There will always be closeminded patients, but these techniques will help the "fence-sitters" commit themselves to dealing with their addictions.

BIOLOGICAL RISK INTERVENTIONS

Genetic Influences

Educational approaches are the primary psychological interventions with biological risk factors. Patients with an extensive family history of substance dependence or significant physical dependence on substances may have inherent biological characteristics that preceded their addictions. Compared with alcoholics with no family history of the addiction, familial alcoholics may exhibit a higher reactivity to stress or stimulation, experience more reinforcing effects from alcohol, or display hyperactive symptoms such as restlessness or poor attention. The combination of these factors can create feelings of frustration, lack of control, and a sense of impending doom. Without being technical, the therapist should introduce the following points about genetic influences early in recovery:

1. Genetic risk factors precede addiction and exist independent of

one's behavior. This does not imply that the patient is powerless, as these risk factors do not explain all of addiction. They should be understood rather than feared, particularly in rearing one's own children.

2. Individuals who developed an affinity and great tolerance for alcohol or drugs at an early age may actually show less effects of use as they progress. Such individuals may deny their addiction on the basis of these lesser effects and should be made aware that addiction goes beyond a person's biological capacities.

3. Associated factors in familial alcoholics such as hyperactivity or antisocial behavior need to be considered as they affect the patient's perceptions of the addiction and ability to deal with frustration.

Withdrawal

In combination with possible genetic factors, one's knowledge about withdrawal symptoms can affect the course of recovery. In addictions to drugs such as alcohol or benzodiazepines, withdrawal is potentially life threatening if not properly treated. With heroin, patients may overestimate withdrawal effects even though they are not life threatening. With cocaine, addicts may underestimate their potential for relapse due to the absence of physical withdrawal symptoms.

Misperceptions can create higher risk in two ways. First, the user who *underestimates* withdrawal effects may not be prepared for physical consequences such as seizures or extreme craving. Those who *overestimate* withdrawal may experience lower self-efficacy and surrender to their insecure feelings. Patients should therefore be encouraged to view withdrawal as a process that varies by

1. *drug* — The significance of withdrawal is quite different for cocaine versus drugs such as benzodiazepines or alcohol.
2. *setting* — Exposure to high availability situations will intensify the discomfort of withdrawal, while detoxification within a safe environment will expedite recovery from withdrawal.
3. *time* — The acute withdrawal effects of most drugs run their course within one week, but a milder, protracted withdrawal state may replace it over the following months.
4. *coping style* — Addicts who tend to somatize, experience high levels of anxiety, or use limited tools for coping may find the effects less tolerable than those who are able to communicate their discomforts and seek nonchemical alternatives.

Even those who navigate the acute withdrawal course without great difficulty may still be at risk for protracted withdrawal. The level of dysfunction is dependent on the substances used and the degree of progress made during the early stages of abstinence. The behavioral signs of protracted withdrawal are extensive and potentially debilitating. The following symptoms should be monitored:

- poor short-term memory
- lack of concentration
- insomnia
- anxious or depressed feelings
- distractibility
- restlessness
- irritability
- difficulty understanding abstract concepts (e.g., "letting go" and "spirituality")
- poor problem solving (under- or overreacting to stress)
- difficulties retaining newly learned information

Because these symptoms are almost universal, patients should be taught that they are likely to occur. Some patients may be dismayed to learn that there is a negative side to recovery and try to ignore these new challenges. They may accuse the therapist of being discouraging or pessimistic about their chances for recovery. These individuals need to assess their relapse risk more objectively and be encouraged to discuss their insecurities about relapse. The above-mentioned symptoms typically represent short-term rather than long-term obstacles to recovery. Interventions to improve memory, problem solving, or relaxation should be more intensive within the first few months. A focus on day-to-day coping takes precedence over discussion of deep-seated issues relating to family trauma or psychopathology.

What methods are effective in coping with protracted withdrawal? Maintaining abstinence will be the primary concern, as a return to usage can potentially begin the whole cycle again. Maintaining balanced eating, exercise, work, and sleeping patterns will provide a basis for improved physical functioning. Stress management techniques such as relaxation and time management will help the patient sort priorities and reduce confusion. Communication skills are important because clients often require feedback and reassurance when experiencing protracted withdrawal symptoms. Such reality testing can defuse thoughts such as "I think that I am going crazy" and "Nothing makes sense anymore."

Sleep and memory problems are probably the most troubling impediments related to protracted withdrawal. Sleep is often disrupted by nighttime awakening or nightmares (usually involving graphic scenes of alcohol or drug use). Many recovering alcoholics and addicts find themselves leaping out of bed in a cold sweat, feeling as if they are under the influence of alcohol or drugs. They often feel guilty, as if they had relapsed. This common occurrence does not signify a lack of motivation, but is the rebound effect of dream sleep in the early stages of abstinence. Education, relaxation strategies, and development of a regular cycle of activity and rest are probably the best interventions for such sleep problems.

Short-term memory problems can interfere with integration of information that the patient will use in recovery. The flow of information is particularly intense during early stages of recovery (when the client will be least likely to remember it). To help with this phase, several strategies should be implemented:

- Be repetitive.
- Be as concise and concrete as possible.
- Present information in a personally relevant manner, that is, instead of listing the medical consequences of addiction, review only those that apply to the patient.
- Encourage the patient to keep a "Sobriety Journal" (Daley, 1988) reviewing important events, experiences, feelings, and impressions about recovery. If not recorded, even the most important breakthroughs can vanish from memory.
- Preface and summarize each session with the patient's goals and accomplishments.

Craving

Craving is inevitable because of one major reason: The cues associated with alcohol and drug use are virtually unlimited and unavoidable. Anything, no matter how innocent or seemingly unconnected to drugs, can trigger usage. Physical objects, thoughts, feelings, places, people, times, the five senses, or memories can all lead to craving. Alcoholics and addicts are keenly aware of the ubiquity of relapse cues. Some even complain that the "drunkalogues" of A.A. set them off. They often ask, "How can you avoid it?" But this begs the question, because the main concern should be *minimization,* and not avoidance, of risk.

Minimizing risk requires an understanding of the presence of dangerous cues. Assuming that avoidance is not possible, patients should be provided with a variety of behavioral options should cravings develop. These behavioral options are based on the following principles:

- Anything can trigger craving, so one needs a variety of techniques. Knowing only one method is inadequate.
- Avoidance is not always possible. One needs to gain an understanding of cravings rather than running from them.
- Craving needs to be broken down into parts. How is it experienced

physically, cognitively, and behaviorally? These components are not the same for everyone.
• Fighting craving through willpower is a losing battle. Many refer to the internal debates that they have when confronted with an urge. These debates consume energy better spent on recovery. It is better to join with thoughts of indulging rather than trying to negate them. Alcoholics Anonymous calls this "thinking through the drink."

Several methods are effective in coping with craving. Marlatt (1985c) uses a technique known as "urge surfing." This technique is based on the notion that attempting to block an urge out of one's mind can actually increase it. Referring to this willpower approach, Ludwig (1988) said, "The picture of not doing triggers an image of doing what the individual is resolved not to do" (p. 96). It is therefore better to do something affirmative. Urge surfing takes place in three steps: (a) assuming a relaxing position to notice which parts of the body are experiencing the urge, (b) focusing on one part of the body where the urge is felt and labeling the sensations, and (c) continuing in this way through each part of the body that is affected by the urge. This method helps the individual "surf" through the cravings until they disappear naturally.

The use of imagery constitutes another effective way to counter craving. The patient is encouraged to develop an image of a situation or consequence of substance use that decreases the desire to surrender to the craving. Images may involve punishment or reward. This technique is effective only if a vivid image is obtained, so it is important to determine the sensory components of the image with great clarity. The patient is asked to describe the smells, sounds, sights, tastes, and physical feel of the situation. The situation should be highly personalized and relevant to substance use. For instance, a punishing image might involve a serious hangover, arguments with family members, losing a job, or getting arrested. A rewarding image might involve having an enjoyable time with family members, buying something with money that has been saved, or being complimented on one's improved appearance.

Imagery can be used in a more formal way through covert sensitization (Rimmele, Miller, & Dougher, 1989). This procedure involves four phases: (a) construction of drinking stimulus scenes (highlighting drinking cues) and sensitization scenes (e.g., nausea or negative emotional reactions), (b) pairing or drinking and sensitization scenes to create physical discomfort, (c) escape from the drinking scene through imagining a healthy alternative behavior *after* the patient experiences discomfort, and (d) avoidance of the drinking scene through imagining a healthy alternative behavior *before* the patient experiences discomfort. This approach has advantages over simple imagery because it creates realistic physical sensations and emotional reactions that can build real-life coping skills.

Distraction is another common method, but it has advantages and disadvantages. Because craving is usually a short-term experience, one needs only to disrupt the momentum of the craving for a short time to be successful. Many alcoholics speak of how they worked through their craving by speaking to a sponsor, visiting a friend, or going for a walk. When craving is a passing thought, this approach is useful. However, some individuals organize their lives around distraction, which violates the principle that cues for craving cannot be avoided. They may resort to excessive work, eating, or other compulsive behavior. When the individual finally requires some rest from the new compulsive behavior, the threat of relapse is even greater because he or she has a void to fill. Distraction should therefore be used only as a stopgap method, not as a way of life. The latter implies that the addict or alcoholic lacks the self-efficacy to master troublesome situations.

Sensation Seeking

Everyone who treats addicts and alcoholics eventually encounters someone who says, "I don't know if I can stop using. I'm the kind of person who likes to be where the action is. If I get straight, all I can picture is a boring life." For sensation-seeking people, boredom is the essential question about recovery. Having developed a lifestyle that stressed high stimulation and activity, why should they welcome serenity, relaxation, and peace? For these individuals, the goal is to live an *unbalanced* life.

Relapse prevention for such clients necessitates a three-pronged strategy: (a) assessment of the individual's definition of boredom and its relationship to substance use, (b) development of a new "bank" of activities, and (c) development of behavioral coping strategies for boredom.

Sensation seekers invariably have a low threshold for boredom, that is, they become bored at levels that normal people would consider adequately stimulating or interesting. Because drug and alcohol use requires more risk taking, these individuals may have trouble disengaging "action" from addiction. The therapist's first job is to point out that substance use usually restricts one's experiences to substance-related situations and that recovery usually includes exposure to new and interesting activities. Much of what sensation seekers call exciting is rule breaking or life threatening, so it is important to stress that such risk taking can involve jail, injury, or even death (all rather unstimulating consequences).

Sensation seekers are often surprised to find that there are many previously untried activities that are stimulating. Many drugs actually dull experiences, requiring an increasing level of stimulation for users to achieve the desired effect. When they become abstinent, they find that they actually enjoy simple activities such as family gatherings, reading, sports, or going to the movies.

Finally, sensation seekers can build skills to cope with boredom just as with any other emotional state. Boredom can be experienced as an irritating, agitating feeling. Relaxation training and biofeedback are useful techniques in helping one combat it. Meditation can also be used to help sensation seekers with their distractibility and poor concentration, both of which are evident under low stimulation conditions.

Boredom can also arise from poor time management. Given a span of time to fill, sensation seekers operate in fits and starts rather than evenly allotting time for activities. Scheduling activities in a more regular fashion will distribute stimulation and help improve moderation.

Physical Health

Although a discussion of physical health is beyond the scope of this book, several issues concerning early recovery should be mentioned. First, physical recovery should be part of the recovery plan. Poor nutrition, inadequate management of physical disorders, and insufficient exercise can lower one's quality of life, increasing the risk of relapse. With a biopsychosocial approach, biological, psychological, and social systems all need to be functional in order to minimize relapse. This means that treatments for nicotine addiction and obesity are *not* optional components of a recovery plan. I regard as ludicrous the notion that an alcoholic or addict should quit one addiction at a time; this approach is not used with any other drug.

Second, the way an addict or alcoholic interacts with physicians, dentists, and other medical personnel should be carefully scrutinized. Recovering patients, particularly when schooled in the disease model, need to be careful not to assume a passive patient role. Instead, they should be active in asking about medications and treatments, especially those that might involve addictive substances. I have suggested that patients complete a written synopsis of their drug histories *prior* to any appointment with a physician and to make copies for all medical professionals treating them. This action prevents the incomplete history gathering in a crisis that could potentially result in prescription of questionable medications.

Third, the decision to use medication should be made cooperatively by the patient and the physician. Sometimes there is little choice and the self-help philosophy of avoiding all medications cannot be maintained. In these cases, however, the danger of relapse can be minimized if the addict or alcoholic has honestly given a complete history to a physician knowledgeable about addiction and judicious about prescribing medication.

PSYCHOLOGICAL RISK
INTERVENTIONS

Expectancy

A person's beliefs about the effects of alcohol or drugs on behavior or emotions can exert a powerful influence over his or her recovery behavior. Some of these beliefs are mentioned openly, but the most hazardous ones are those that remain unstated. Patients may not even question their veracity. Sometimes social pressure from friends will force them to keep their uncertainties private. Here are some examples from cocaine users:

"Sniffing cocaine is not addictive."

"Cocaine improves your sex life."

"Cocaine helps me be creative."

"My relationships with cocaine users are more interesting."

"Cocaine improves my physical functioning."

These expectancies are usually at odds with actual consequences and behavior, which may be physical, occupational, social, financial, familial, psychological, or spiritual. It is therefore worthwhile for patients to take a survey among significant others about actual consequences of alcohol and drug use. For instance, if patients believe that cocaine makes them less depressed, they should complete a "Consequences Form" (see Appendix C). This form requires patients to list perceived positive and negative effects of the drug and the percentage of times they thought they experienced these effects. The last column requests feedback from another person familiar with the patient's behavior while he or she was under the influence of the drug (with a corresponding percentage). This task may also be conducted in a group setting with feedback from other addicts and alcoholics about the percentage of time they experienced these effects. The discrepancies that usually arise can then be addressed and used as an opportunity for education and insight.

It is useful to distinguish between large-scale and abstract versus small-scale and concrete consequences (Schiffman, 1988). Large-scale consequences include death, illness, and significant loss. Small-scale consequences include relatively minor physical consequences (e.g., hangovers), losses that can be recovered, or temporary emotional reactions (e.g., superficial guilt). Those who have progressed well into their addiction may have great difficulty distinguishing between large-scale and small-scale losses because large-scale losses are the only ones left.

Negative expectancies about treatment and self-help can potentially lead to helpless or trapped feelings, evident in statements such as "I tried treatment; it didn't work before so why should it work this time?" or "A.A. is a drag. I think those people are addicted to meetings." Although the past treatment might have been inadequate or the patient unmotivated, a more fruitful approach might be to review how the patient could have utilized treatment better. Presenting relapse as incomplete assessment and each treatment as a new step toward recovery is preferable to lamenting the patient's lack of motivation. For a patient to hear "You must have learned something—you stayed sober for 3 months" builds self-efficacy. A response such as "Maybe you'll get it right this time" encourages a passive acceptance of fate, as if the patient were a receptacle for new information. Treatment that is presented as a collaborative process will encourage active decision making and result in a sense of ownership about change. This approach requires mutual goal setting, sharing of formal and informal assessments, and attention to consumerism in treatment. Under these conditions, compliance is part of a mutual agreement rather than the result of a manipulative or confrontative process.

Coping with High-Risk Situations

This section covers four major classes of coping skills that are critical to maintaining abstinence in high risk situations: (a) problem solving, (b) cognitive coping skills, (c) social skills, and (d) emotional and stress management. Clinicians can determine particular high risk situations through structured interviews, roleplays, or paper-and-pencil assessments that were reviewed in chapter 5. These situations can then be ranked according to formal scoring or subjective estimates of risk provided by clients.

Problem Solving Problem solving is considered a useful way to enhance coping skills within clinical populations (Goldfried & Davison, 1976). Problem solving is a systematic approach used to identify problems, "brainstorm" and implement solutions, and evaluate the results. D'Zurilla and Goldfried (1971) break down the problem-solving sequence into orientation (recognizing a problem), definition (defining the problem), generation of alternatives ("brainstorming"), decision making (selecting the best alternative), and verification (evaluating the results). For treatment purposes, clinicians can summarize problem solving in eight questions:

1. Is there a problem?
2. What do I want to happen?
3. What are the possible ways of reaching this goal?
4. Which alternative is best?
5. What will happen if I carry this alternative out?
6. Am I capable of doing it?

7. How do I do it?
8. Did it work?

Any disruption of this sequence can result in an ineffective response, which can in turn increase the risk of relapse. Table 6.1 lists types of disruptions with reasons for each.

To learn whether clients have problem-solving skills the therapist can present them with hypothetical substance-related situations. Chaney (1989) has developed the Situational Competency Test in which patients listen to 16 audiotaped, written, or orally presented risky alcohol or drug situations and imagine what they would say or do. These situations encompass a variety of dilemmas, including frustrating and angering situations, social pressure, negative physical states, and temptations. The following is an example: "You are eating at a good restaurant on a special occasion with some friends. The waitress comes over and says, 'Drinks before dinner?' Everyone else orders one. All eyes seem to be on you. What do you do?" (Chaney, 1989, p. 211).

Both the client and clinician rate the effectiveness of the responses on a 1 to 5 scale (no response/poor to very effective). With low ratings, the clinician can then model more effective responses and role play the situation with the client. Personalizing these situations will make the roleplays more realistic and allow the client to practice more relevant skills. In a group format, this method can be quite constructive and instructive because the opportunity for feedback from peers. In all cases, the therapist

Table 6.1. Disruptions in Problem Solving

Stage of Problem Solving	Possible Disruptions
Orientation	Lack of awareness of physical, emotional, and social cues Social or cultural learning factors
Definition	Poor assessment of facts in problem situation Lack of vision as to desired result Impulsivity or excessive deliberation ("paralysis by analysis") Denial or rationalization Difficulty breaking down problem into manageable parts
Generating Alternatives	Rigidity within a frame of reference Impulsivity Excessive evaluation of options
Decision Making	Impulsivity Poor judgment of possible outcomes Lack of self-efficacy
Verification	Difficulty determining success Jumping to conclusions Lack of inclusion of feedback

should try to arrive at a set of principles rather than just specific responses. For instance, if certain clients test control by attending drinking parties, they should understand not only the responses that get them out of the situation, but understand the need for prevention through avoidance. The following list of principles should be stressed:

- Alcohol or drug use should *never* be considered a viable option in problem solving.
- When avoiding a risky activity or situation, a healthful behavior or situation should replace it.
- Prevention is preferable to escape in problem situations.
- No response is always effective. The most important consideration is that one has tried the best option available.
- Make use of social support.
- Change your behavior and your attitudes will follow. It is much more difficult to change your attitudes first.
- Be honest.
- Look for the simplest and most straightforward solution.

Problem-solving feedback can be furnished in a more formal manner. Clients can be presented with a situation and asked to complete a "Problem-Solving Alternatives" list. Table 6.2 lists responses for the following hypothetical situation:

> Frank is a 25-year-old married construction worker who has two young children. He recently stopped drinking and using cocaine, but is struggling with early recovery. With his job, family responsibilities, and A.A. meetings, he has little time to spend with his wife. He is unsure how to approach her, as she is still angry about his last binge. He has few friends left because he is trying to avoid the party scene. He feels lost, life isn't fun, and he doesn't know himself like he once thought he did. One day a friend stops by Frank's work site and tells him that an old friend is in town. There will be a large get-together and Frank is invited. What does Frank do?

This approach allows review of a range of options and forces the client to evaluate options individually. For instance, the client may reject solutions that are potentially effective because he misperceives the consequences ("I can't say no if my friend offers me a drink because then he'll think I'm stuck up.") The clinician can then respond to faulty perceptions relating to particular responses.

Cognitive Coping Skills Alcoholics Anonymous promotes the notion that "stinking thinking" is a sign of relapse. When broken down, the concept of "stinking thinking" represents poor cognitive coping abilities. Cognitive coping can preempt negative thinking by distinguishing lapses from relapses, maintaining accurate perceptions of self-efficacy and outcome ex-

Table 6.2. Problem-Solving Alternatives List

Phase	Question	Response
Orientation	Is there a problem?	Yes. Frank is trying to juggle family and recovery.
Definition	What is the problem?	Lack of time. Uncertainty toward wife. Lack of friends. Lack of fun. An invitation to a party.
Generation	What is the goal?	To stay straight. To improve communication with his wife. To manage his time. To have fun.
	What are the alternatives?	Find new activities. Discuss his dilemma more openly with his wife. Discuss the party invitation with a friend in Alcoholics Anonymous. Develop a schedule with some free time.
Decision Making	Which one first?	Deal with the party invitation first because it is the most immediate threat to recovery.
	What might happen?	His sponsor might talk him out of going to the party.
Verification	How will Frank know whether it worked?	He will avoid the party. He will still be straight. He will be in a position to address the other problems.

pectancy, awareness of "seemingly irrelevant decisions" (Monti, Abrams, Kadden, & Cooney, 1989), and positive "self-talk." Clinicians can teach these skills systematically to individuals with tendencies toward self-defeating thoughts.

The concern with absolute sobriety can intensify short-term mistakes (slips or lapses) so that they become transformed into full-blown relapses. Rather than considering a lapse an indication of failure, a patient should view it as an indication of incomplete assessment or a mistake. Clients can benefit greatly from reframing the lapse as a place to *begin* an inquiry instead of a place to give up. Lapsers are likely to feel much guilt (abstinence violation effect), so judgmental attitudes will only enhance their negative self-evaluations. Marlatt (1985c) stresses the importance of reattributing a lapse to external, specific, and controllable factors. Clients should therefore be discouraged from labeling themselves or interpreting the lapse as a fateful event. Guiding clients through the people, places, situations, thoughts, and feelings leading to the lapse can be instructive and send a message that recovery is a learning process.

The progression from lapse to relapse can be avoided through relatively simple and logical steps: (a) recognizing the "smoke" (lapse) as the first indication of a "fire" (relapse), (b) removing oneself from the risky situation, (c) analyzing events leading up to the lapse, and (d) asking for help and feedback from a supportive person. In keeping with a prevention philosophy, clients can complete a "relapse contract" with a friend, sponsor, coworker, or relative prior to any difficulty. The cosigner should be nonjudgmental and readily available. A sample relapse contract can be found in Appendix D.

To benefit from this new knowledge, the client must feel capable of handling the difficult circumstances leading to the substance use. A combination of self-efficacy and accurate outcome expectancy is essential in selecting an effective response. These responses may involve skills such as anger management, refusal of addicting substances, positive thinking, or coping with craving. Several principles can be used to instill a sense of mastery with such skills:

1. Review past attempts at solving the same problem. Although addicted individuals are likely to ascribe failure to *all* past attempts, they may have actually achieved some success. Focusing on available skills rather than inadequacies can improve the client's prospects.

2. Model the response or give concrete examples. If the client is angry at someone, a suggestion such as "Let go of your anger" may be too abstract. An alternative such as "Avoid using profanity" is much more manageable.

3. Emphasize proximal goal setting, also known as "One day at a time" in A.A. jargon. Breaking down the response by time, intensity, length, or complexity will result in greater success and self-confidence.

4. Teach clients how to seek, listen to, and integrate feedback. Many addicted individuals become defensive, isolate themselves, or have poor listening skills, all of which preclude an accurate measure of their behavior.

5. Discourage "black-or-white" thinking. Learning a new skill is a process that is dynamic and never complete. Even if one does learn the appropriate skill, there is no guarantee that it will succeed. As a result, preparation for failure experiences should be included.

Seemingly irrelevant decisions (SIDs) can be difficult to detect because they are often subconscious. They are often presented in a plausible manner. For instance, one addict with a gambling problem relapsed after meeting some friends accidentally in a shopping center where there was an off-track betting establishment. He decided to bet on a horse race, an activity that later led him to go to a bar and have a drinking binge. He certainly did not plan to see these friends, but made several unhealthful decisions with little self-awareness. An alcoholic relapsed when he visited his son, who let him sleep on the living room sofa next to the liquor cabinet. This alcoholic noticed the bottles, examined one for awhile, and eventually succumbed to an urge to drink. In both of these cases, the relapse began innocently, but built momentum as each unhealthful decision was made.

It seems logical that an addicted person will not experience an SID if his decision has no chance of resulting in substance use. In addition, different people, places, feelings, and thoughts have different proximities to substance use. If an individual interacts with only low proximity factors, a SID will be unlikely. Patients can be asked to rank the degree of proximity different factors have to substance use on a scale from 1 to 5 (1 = no connection, 5 = high proximity). They are then instructed to seek feedback from an interested party any time they make a decision that places them in contact with a factor greater than 3.

In recent years, emphasis on getting patients to have positive conversations with themselves has increased. However, the negative thinking is so ingrained that it is difficult to banish. Addicts and alcoholics have an intimate awareness of their internal dialogues, so much so that they can recall their thoughts verbatim. Instead of progressing to substance use, these thoughts can be used as stimuli for alternative responses such as exercise, relaxation, or conversation with a friend.

The "Famous Quotes" exercise can be used to identify thoughts that create an urge to drink. When the patient verbalizes these thoughts, the clinician points them out and assigns a self-monitoring assignment. The patient keeps a running list of situations in which these thoughts occur and develops a list of positive thoughts that can replace them. Some examples are listed in Table 6.3.

Sometimes these internal dialogues are so automatic that to replace them with positive thinking requires deliberate use of prepared lines. Ludwig (1989) suggests the following "sobriety scripts":

1. *negative consequences*—invoke embarrassing, shameful, or uncontrolled incidents, such as "The last time I drank at a wedding, I embarrassed the bride and groom."
2. *benefits of sobriety*—focus on positive consequences, such as "If I stay off drugs, I can save money to buy a car."
3. *rationality*—convince oneself of the choice that one has made to resist substance use, such as "I'm determined to stay straight and I can't go back to the old life."
4. *avoid the first drink*—focus on abstinence and avoid testing oneself: "If I take that first drink, I won't be able to stop."
5. *prayer*—appeal to a higher power to maintain abstinence: "God, help me get through this difficult situation."

Table 6.3. Famous Quotes

Negative Thought	Alternative
"I'll just test myself."	"Even if you 'pass,' think of all the past failures."
"I deserve a reward for working so hard."	"Find another way to reward yourself."
"How can I watch a football game without a beer?"	"You usually drink too much when you watch football; then you can't enjoy it."
"My wife drives me to drink."	"No one forces you to drink. You use it as an excuse."
"My friends don't think that I have a drug problem."	"Of course they don't. They have drug problems, too."
"I can't control this craving."	"You've done it before. It will last only a few minutes."
"How am I supposed to have fun now?"	"Think of all the things that you never did because of drinking and drugging."
"I'll be a boring person if I stay away from drinking."	"It was boring to sit on the same bar stool every day."

Social Skills Social skills affect the ways in which the alcoholic or addict perceives, interprets, and exchanges information with other people. Perception and interpretation are guided by a person's belief system and past experience with a particular situation, while the exchange of information is based on the knowledge and performance of effective social behavior.

Bellack, Hersen, and Himmelhoch (1978) divide social skills into four categories: (a) expressive elements, (b) receptive elements, (c) interactive balance, and (d) cognitive factors. Expressive elements include voice quality, eye contact, facial expressions, and the content of the message. Receptive elements include perceiving and interpreting information. Interactive balance refers to the timing of responses, for example, interruptions or overly long pauses. Cognitive elements include socialization messages (family or cultural beliefs about self-expression), self-efficacy, and social perception (awareness of social interaction norms). These categories can be summarized in the following four questions:

1. How clearly is the message expressed?
2. How clearly is the message interpreted?
3. How well are responses timed?
4. How do the person's thoughts help or hurt communication?

These questions should be evaluated from three viewpoints. First, are social skills deficits evident in addiction-specific situations or are they generalized? Deficits that are addiction specific tend to follow substance ingestion. For instance, drinking may lead to socially inept or unacceptable behavior. In these situations, abstinence will lead to a reversal of this behavior. Generalized deficits arise even in nonsubstance situations and would probably be present even without alcohol. Some clients may have difficulty conversing with people while sober and drink to build "liquid courage." Others may become immobilized when they attempt to express intimate feelings. In these cases, social skills training requires a discussion of outcome expectancies as well as behavioral interventions such as modeling, roleplaying, and practice. Assertive skills are similar to expectancies relating to the "serenity" advocated by Alcoholics Anonymous—honesty, acceptance, and self-knowledge.

Second, social skills training tends to be individually focused. A therapist can enhance this focus by pointing out how different types of communication are treated by different types of people. Clients can benefit from clear descriptions of assertive, aggressive, passive, and passive-aggressive behavior, not only in terms of individual behavior but also in terms of how individuals exhibiting these types interact in relationships. Combinations of the latter three have particular implications for relapse prevention:

1. A *passive-passive relationship* will exhibit little risk taking and emotional sharing. Relapse will tend to occur in a quiet and indirect manner. To avoid it, mutual discussion of "taboo" topics such as "closet" drinking and dishonesty should be initiated.

2. An *aggressive-aggressive relationship* will be marked by power struggles and direct resistance. Relapse will tend to occur as impulsive, volatile behavior. Members of these relationships need to consider openly that substance abuse is harmful to both parties and that further escalation will only encourage increased acting out.

3. A *passive-aggressive–passive-aggressive relationship* will be characterized by game playing and indirect, vindictive behavior. Relapse may be used as a manipulative ploy, with the relapser placing blame on the other party. Individuals in such a relationship need to be cautioned against using substances as substitutes for direct expression of anger.

4. An *aggressive–passive-aggressive relationship* will appear to be controlled by the aggressive individual, but will actually be controlled by the passive-aggressive member. The latter will manipulate through substance use, while the former is more likely to use substances to act out frustration. Relapse can be avoided if both parties realize that their tactics foster a "win-lose" philosophy that undercuts the social support needed for the mutual benefits of recovery.

Third, as a result of their all-or-none thinking, many addicts and alcoholics lack effective interpersonal problem-solving (negotiation) skills. In *Getting to Yes,* Fisher and Ury (1981) stress the importance of one's philosophical approach to bargaining in affecting results. For instance, some people adopt a "soft" bargaining position, as they focus on concessions, agreement, and avoidance of confrontation. "Hard" bargainers focus on victory, willpower, distrust, and personal attacks. The best way to maximize results for both participants is through "principled" bargaining, which separates people from the problem, invents options for mutual gain, and utilizes objective criteria.

In order to help recovering people identify communication blocks, I encourage them to review their interpersonal philosophies. These philosophies may arise from a dysfunctional family life, numerous losses, or a "streetwise" mentality. The following are some examples of beliefs that may impede interpersonal problem solving:

"Life stinks and then you die."

"People can't be trusted."

"It's a dog-eat-dog world."

"Get them before they get you."

"Don't get mad, get even."

"The best defense is a good offense."

We then discuss how these philosophies can prevent solutions to problems the clients are experiencing with friends and family. Many do not even question whether these outlooks are correct. Because it is difficult to blend negative convictions with recovery, the following alternatives can be supplied:

"Life has brought some bad times but a bad attitude will only make it worse."

"If I keep hanging around with alcoholics, I certainly will have trouble trusting people."

"Competition may be good for business, but it gets in the way of your personal life."

"If you go on the attack, you may lose a potential friend."

"Getting even only makes your resentments worse."

Emotional and Stress Management The concept of balance is central to a successful recovery. Marlatt (1985d) defines balance as an equality between pleasant activities that a person does for himself (wants) and external demands that are experienced as stress (shoulds). When someone attends only to wants, he becomes irresponsible. When he attends only to shoulds, he becomes self-sacrificing. The larger the inequality, the greater the risk of relapse. The individual may resort to addictive behavior to restore a sense of balance.

Imbalances arise from a variety of sources, including (a) emotional mismanagement, (b) mismanagement of stressful life events, (c) poor health habits, (d) poor lifestyle pacing, and (e) a lack of meaning. Those who develop the skills to manage these imbalances effectively will typically stabilize their recoveries earlier and be more resilient to disruptive events.

Emotional management is particularly important with anger, guilt, sadness, loneliness, and tension. Early recovery presents people with a disturbing mix of feelings that appear to result from abstinence but which actually represent consequences of addiction. Alcoholics and addicts need to be reminded that feelings do not necessarily arise in a direct way, but often masquerade as vague somatic problems (headaches, fatigue, or gastrointestinal disturbances), escapist behavior (excessive sleep, reading, or daydreaming), or behavior opposite to the actual feeling (such as smiling when angry or depressed). Verbal and nonverbal expressions should match actual emotions; otherwise there is a risk of indirect expression. In these cases, a recovering person is not attending to wants but is transforming emotion into more easily discussed problems. The clinician can redirect the client by showing how these transformations exacerbate hidden emotions and increase the urge to use substances to create an artificial sense of balance.

Relapsed alcoholics and addicts frequently blame stressful life events for relapse. Relapsers experience more life events than nonrelapsers (Moos, Finney, & Cronkite, 1990); however, it is not events, but *perceptions* of events, that motivate substance use. As these perceptions become more negative, imbalances grow. There are some recovering people who seem to have horrible luck—they lose their jobs, relatives die, or they have accidents—but many of these individuals remain abstinent. On the other hand, some recovering people seem to relapse at the slightest provocation. In reality this group has probably been experiencing a number of high risk episodes that reach the overload point when the provocation occurs. A review of seemingly irrelevant decisions, imbalances, or high risk situations can often yield an accurate assessment of the reasons for the relapse. Clinicians can encourage clients to regard extreme reactions to life events as indicators of impending relapse.

Poor health habits represent a continuation of addictive patterns. A lack of exercise, inadequate nutrition, insufficient rest and relaxation, and unhealthful associated addictions such as smoking frequently accompany substance addiction. Inadequate bodily functioning will make normal external demands seem more taxing and increase the stressful or "should" side of the equation. Good nutrition, exercise, and sleep and relaxation plans can decrease stress and provide time for pleasant activites, or "wants."

Lifestyle pacing refers to the way an individual allots time for activities.

Some people structure their lives with a dense schedule of activities, leaving them rushed and fatigued. These individuals experience life as full of "shoulds." Others have little initiative and frequently find themselves bored and inactive. These individuals do not have enough "shoulds." A time management plan that allows for even spacing of activities and a balance of should and wants will minimize the risk of relapse.

Finally, many recovering people find that they develop a sense of meaning (or spirituality) in their lives when they become sober. Others have difficulty understanding the reason they are getting sober. Alcoholics Anonymous stresses the importance of a higher power that helps one cope with addiction. Some find this through religion, while others look to their social support group. In either case, the aim is for the individual to stop fighting addiction and to begin to accept it. Developing a sense of belonging allows one to feel important, accepted, and loved, qualities which are notably lacking in alcoholics and addicts. However, spirituality needs to develop as a result of increased self-awareness and self-actualization. Those who transform themselves through overnight realizations or sudden insights will often relapse because they have not integrated this knowledge into a new lifestyle. Lasting change is seldom dramatic or quick, and spirituality appears to be a quality that requires much time to develop.

Management of Family Dysfunction The first consideration in marital or family intervention is whether to include members of the family. Family members should be excluded only when they refuse involvement or the addicted family member does not allow the others to participate. Assessment and intervention, particularly for relapse prevention, should involve anyone with whom the addict or alcoholic is living. Family intervention should not be reserved for families with serious conflict or disruption, as the triggers for substance use are frequently subtle.

Marital or family therapy is more likely to be effective when there is social stability: The alcoholic or addict is employed, older, dealing with addiction that is more serious and of longer duration, at least high school educated, and living with a spouse who is not alcoholic, drug addicted, or psychiatrically impaired (O'Farrell, 1990). When there is a history of domestic violence, the therapist must assess the risk of injury based on the addicted individual's behavior while abstinent. Continuing violence precludes effective relapse prevention and requires contracting with the family to prevent further aggression and to encourage appropriate expression of anger. Many alcoholics and addicts do not meet all these criteria, but treatment can be altered by moving more slowly, individualizing interventions, or addressing resistances or obstacles as they appear (O'Farrell, 1990).

Marital and family interventions can be either substance based or relationship based. Interventions related to substance use focus on educating family members about the relapse process, developing relapse contracts, and decreasing family behaviors that trigger substance use. Relationship-related interventions focus on reducing conflict, increasing positive interaction, and building problem-solving skills.

Family members are subject to the same mythology about relapse as those in recovery. They experience a similar process of denial and tend to minimize their role in the addiction. They may make the addict or alcoholic a scapegoat, an action implying that the family will return to normal when abstinence begins. They may have unrealistic expectations that the recovering person will adjust to his new life smoothly without negative consequences for the rest of the family. When asked about potential *negative* effects of recovery, family members have difficulty understanding the question. They often require education about the following points:

1. Recovery means that family problems *not* associated with addiction may be exposed. If family members approach their problems honestly, they will not be able to blame everything on the addicted person. For instance, family members may have to scrutinize their own substance use.

2. Although the recovering person is now available to understand family concerns, he or she may have only limited ability to correct ongoing problems because of difficulties in the early stages of abstinence.

3. Because many families organize themselves around the addiction, they may have to change *their* behavior to accommodate recovery. For instance, children who received no discipline during the alcoholic's drunkenness may not have the same freedom during recovery.

4. Marriages do not necessarily improve during abstinence. Many couples have never known each other in a sober state and may have difficulty adjusting to each other. Even during good recoveries, many marriages break up. The key factor appears to be the relative rate of change of the partners: The partner who is resisting change will often be rejected.

5. Recovering people often develop new relationships within the context of self-help groups, religious involvement, or exposure to new activities. Family members may find this different behavior threatening.

Development of relapse contracts and avoidance of family behaviors that trigger substance use can be combined into one step. These behaviors concern attempts to excuse, control, scapegoat, persuade, protect, manipulate, or threaten the addicted person and his or her behavior. These seemingly logical actions actually promote substance use and require their own "relapse prevention." The strategy of intervention is to replace these negative behaviors with positive reinforcers such as mutually enjoyable activities, praise, or rewards (e.g., making a favorite dinner). Family members can assist in relapse prevention by following these suggestions:

1. Avoid nagging, preaching, and scolding. These behaviors make the family member a target rather than a helper.

2. Do not play "detective." This includes searching for alcohol or drugs, kissing the alcoholic to determine whether he or she has been drinking, calling friends of the recovering person to check on his or her whereabouts, or rummaging through wallets or glove compartments to seek evidence of substance use.

3. Do not bring up the recovering person's past misdeeds as a way to attack him or her. Discussion of past events should take place in an atmosphere of understanding. Asking questions such as "Why did you do that?" will not yield satisfactory answers.

4. Know the signs of impending relapse and make an agreement to discuss them if they occur.

5. Encourage personal growth, even if new behaviors are difficult to accept. Avoid statements such as "Are you going to a meeting *again?"* or "I liked you better when you were drinking."

6. Early recovery is demanding. The recovering person will most likely experience mood changes, irritability, frustration, or depressed feelings, and should be allowed some "slack."

7. Family members can "relapse" too; they need to try to prevent the above behaviors.

Some families find that if they can follow these guidelines, they can develop a functional family system. However, others continue to experience communication problems that require another level of intervention. For many families and couples, the first order of business is to reduce conflict. Building communication skills will create a positive climate for change.

Bornstein and Bornstein (1986) suggest four major principles of communication: (a) timeliness (expressing oneself promptly), (b) "marital manners" (affording one's partner the same politeness that one expresses to others), (c) behavioral specification ("I feel ———, when you do ——— in ——— situation"), and (d) "mind reading" (making incorrect assumptions about what one's partner is thinking). These principles can then be applied to behaviors that impede communication, such as nagging, interrupting, sidetracking, insulting, criticizing, or threatening. I have asked couples to list specific statements made by their spouses that trigger their anger. Some examples are "You're a loser," "Remember when you did such-and-such," or "If you didn't drink, we wouldn't have any problems." Couples can then be taught to replace these comments with positive alternatives that communicate flexibility, assertiveness, appreciation, nondefensiveness, and affection.

O'Farrell and Cowles (1989) suggest that families can increase awareness of pleasing behaviors as an antidote to the rancor caused by addiction. They recommend the use of an assignment called "Catch Your Spouse Doing Something Nice," which involves monitoring caring behaviors such as physical affection, helping behavior, or emotional warmth. Spouses discuss these behaviors in therapy sessions and practice acknowledging positive interactions at home. This assignment can be extended by planning shared recreational activities, which have typically been avoided due to the addict's substance use.

Problem-solving skills can be utilized in a corrective or preventive manner. The latter function is especially applicable to relapse prevention because it assumes that there is an ever-present risk of conflict in any relationship. Problem solving encourages families and couples to develop a framework of communication that can be used when any disagreement arises. Bornstein and Bornstein (1986) suggest the following steps:

- Choosing an appropriate time and place for problem solving.
- Recording details of problem-solving sessions.
- Being specific in defining the problem.
- Accepting a mutual definition of the problem and moving toward a solution.
- Specifying goals.
- Considering the broadest range of possible solutions.
- Trying it out, collecting data, and evaluating the outcome.
- If necessary, refining, revising, or renegotiating the agreement.

This style of communication dictates negotiation and compromise, qualities that negate power struggles, intimidation, threats, stalemates, and "cold wars." It avoids the win-lose, black-white mentality that mirrors the extremist behavior of addiction and tends to spiral into eventual substance usage.

Chapter 7

Relapse Prevention with Special Populations

Boys should abstain from all wine
until their eighteenth year, for
it is wrong to add fire to fire.
—Plato

In previous chapters, areas of assessment and technique applicable to any subgrouping of addicted people have been reviewed. Certain relapse issues, however, are specific to different populations. In this chapter important issues in adolescent, female, elderly, dually diagnosed, and impaired professional populations are examined.

ADOLESCENTS

Developmental Differences

Relapse is a high-frequency occurrence in adults. Presumably, many of these adults have attained at least some of the developmental skills needed to survive in this difficult world. However, since adolescents are at an earlier phase of emotional and physical growth, their coping skills, emotional understanding, communication ability, and stress management skills so critical to relapse prevention are underdeveloped. One should not expect recovery messages given to adults to have the same meaning or importance to adolescents. Therapists need to consider the expectancies and goals of young people in tailoring assessment and intervention.

One common mistake is to use fear-oriented messages such as "You will die if you return to drugs" or "You will lose everything." Adolescents seldom take these comments seriously because of their youth and inability to envision such extreme consequences. In fact, scare tactics may *encourage* experimentation (Lex, 1985). Interventions need to be planned to accommodate both the developmental level and the stage of addiction of each adolescent.

McCarthy (1985), discussing smoking prevention, suggests that there are four stages of nicotine addiction: (a) neophyte smoker, (b) experimental smoker, (c) confirmed occasional smoker, and (d) confirmed addicted smoker. Neophyte smokers respond best to fear appeals related to physical health, especially those dealing with immediate physiological consequences of smoking. Experimental smokers respond best to learning refusal skills. Confirmed occasional smokers may be more receptive to communication and decision-making skills. Confirmed addicted smokers may require information about lifestyle changes and the benefits of healthful alternatives. Giving all adolescent smokers the same treatment will result in poorer outcomes. There is no reason to believe that alcoholics and drug addicts would react differently.

McCarthy also distinguishes interventions by age, noting that emotional, physical, and social needs are different at different ages. He suggests that physical messages ("Smoking will make you feel sick") will have greatest impact on preteens ("latency" age), social messages ("Your friends will stay away from you") will be beneficial for pubescent teens, and psychological messages ("Smoking is no way to feel better about yourself") will best address the needs of later teens. The relative importance of these messages at different ages is presented in Figure 7.1.

Peer Pressure

With adults, peer pressure is a noteworthy but relatively less potent relapse predictor than emotional mismanagement. However, peer relationships are powerful predictors of relapse in adolescents. Their friends represent not only a social circle but also an identity and status in the world. An adolescent alcoholic or addict who renounces friendships as well as abused substances risks an almost complete loss of identity.

A recent study of situational factors in relapse showed that most adolescents relapse in the afternoon or evening, in unsupervised settings, and with pretreatment drug friends (Myers & Brown, 1990). They seldom relapse alone. In maintaining abstinence, behavioral (leaving the situation, refusal, and alternative activities) rather than cognitive strategies, such as fear of negative consequences, are more effective. These findings accentuate the need to address concrete and socially oriented strategies with adolescents.

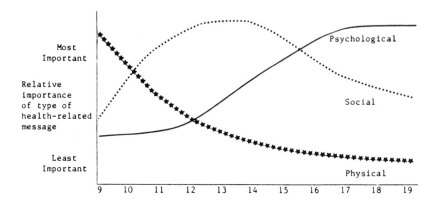

FIGURE 7.1.   Relative importance of physical, psychological, and social health messages as a function of age. From W. J. McCarthy (1985), "The cognitive developmental model and other alternatives to the social skills deficit model of smoking onset." In C. S. Bell and R. Battjes (Eds.), *Prevention Research: Deterring Drug Abuse Among Children and Adolescents* (DHHS Publication No. ADM 87-1334, pp. 153–169). Washington, DC: U.S. Government Printing Office.

Lack of Self-Determination

Teenagers in general have relatively little control over their lives. Their adult guardians usually decide where they will live, where they go to school, whom they live with, what their family responsibilities are, how they manage their money, and sometimes who their friends are.

This lack of self-determination is even more stressful to adolescents in alcoholic or drug-using families. Such adolescents cannot easily leave the abusive or alcoholic living situation, nor can they induce their parents to stop drinking. Teenaged children of alcoholics often must deal with emotional issues related to parental drinking in addition to the temptation of drugs or alcohol in the home. If their friends use drugs, they are likely to become trapped in the school environment also. Moving to another town or befriending an entirely new group of classmates is a daunting task for an adolescent. These obstacles can cause frustration and lead the adolescent to old solutions. Issues of dependency, lack of control, naivete about available resources, and need for social support therefore require extra attention when one is dealing with teenagers.

The Myth of Indestructibility

Most teenagers have difficulty envisioning the consequences of addiction. Unrealistic thinking rising from their incomplete emotional development limits their perception of potential death or serious injury (De Leon & Deitch, 1985). They may view youth as an impenetrable buffer against negative outcomes such as acquired immune deficiency syndrome (AIDS), unwanted pregnancy, and lost relationships. When abstinence from alcohol or drugs is suggested, a teenager may say, "Do you mean that I can't drink or use drugs for *the rest of my life?* What am I supposed to do for fun in the meantime? I still have a lot of years left." As adolescents do not have heavy investments in the future and have relatively little to lose compared to adults, they tend to be shortsighted. Threats, fear tactics, and extremist thinking can often cause them to harden their positions. Adolescents need information about consequences and risks that have impact at their current stage of development. The therapist who explains relapse as an event that could interfere with a teenager's social adjustment, make his or her personality less desirable, or strip away his or her newfound identity has the best chance of success. If adolescents are given assistance with problem-solving skills, the likelihood will increase that they will sort through potential risks effectively.

Multiple Drugs, Multiple Problems

More than 50% of adolescents entering treatment programs report that marijuana is their drug of choice, but most of these adolescents are multiple drug users (Beschner, 1985). About 75% use multiple nonnarcotic drugs in addition to marijuana and alcohol (Hubbard, Cavanaugh, Craddock, & Rachal, 1985), a situation that contributes to their denial, as they tend to isolate the negative effects of one drug rather than envision the full scope of drug use. Convincing adolescents that addiction is a lifestyle rather than a set of experiences may help them assess the overall impact of their substance abuse.

Teenagers tend not to seek treatment on their own; when they do, it is often because of family problems, poor school adjustment, legal entanglements, or negative feelings (alienation, anger, depression, or loneliness). Three-quarters of adolescent substance abusers report one or more drug-related problems, particularly family and school problems (Hubbard et al., 1985). Early onset drug and alcohol problems are often associated with illegal activities, both drug- and nondrug-related (Marks, Daroff, & Granick, 1985). Adolescents, because of their lack of resources, are particularly susceptible to drug dealing and prostitution when they become addicted to cocaine (Gold, 1990). Professionals interested in relapse prevention need to assess these multiple problem areas carefully, especially the ways adolescents support their substance abuse habits and the secretive activities they may engage in and of which they are ashamed.

Experimentation Versus Abuse

A National Institute of Drug Abuse survey of high school students, college students, and young adults showed that by their senior year in high school 92% of the young people sampled have tried alcohol and 57% have tried an illicit drug (Johnston, O'Malley, & Bachman, 1988). By their mid-20s, 75% have used marijuana and 40% have used cocaine. These statistics demonstrate that use of drugs, although a less than healthful form of recreation, is not deviant behavior for most adolescents. Shedler and Block (1990) found that the alienation, impulsivity, and emotional distress of frequent users precedes the initiation of drug use. It is therefore important to establish whether an adolescent's substance abuse is experimental or part of an overall life pattern of maladjustment. Drug education ("Just say no") may assist the teenager who is experimenting with drugs but will probably have little impact on the psychological makeup of the addicted teenager. For this one, the meaning of drug use within a broad pathological pattern needs to be addressed (Shedler & Block, 1990).

Adolescents and Music

There are sensational reports of violence, satanism, and defiance of authority related to rock music, particularly "heavy metal" (King & Flaum, 1988). Most adolescents listen to some variant of this music but relatively few act on or believe in such extreme messages. However, it is important to recognize the intimate connection that drugs and alcohol share with music. Music for adolescents represents an identity, recreational activity, and philosophical statement. Many teenagers combine alcohol and drug use with listening to music to such an extent that music can function as a powerful cue for substance use. Music-related paraphernalia such as T-shirts, patches, belt buckles, and posters can be equally influential. A teenager may not need to listen to a song that glorifies substance use; he or she may need only to associate the song with substance use. Simply banning troublesome music will not address the teenager's recovery needs. It is important to establish the relationship of music to substance use and the perceived meaning of the music. Again, there is no reason to be extreme; one must simply gauge the strength of the music as a cue for substance use.

WOMEN

Recent estimates suggest that male alcoholics outnumber female alcoholics 3 to 1 (Goodwin, 1988). Nearly half of randomly selected callers to a cocaine hotline were women, compared to one third 2 years prior to this survey (Washton & Gold, 1987). Substance abuse trends suggest an increase among women as their cultural and economic opportunities expand (Lex, 1985), but this should not obscure the significant stylistic differences between sexes that offset these substance abuse patterns. These differences are reviewed in the next section.

Substance Use Characteristics

Lex (1985) delineates the following differences between male and female alcoholics:

1. Women typically consume less alcohol than men, drinking less frequently and less continuously.
2. Women begin drinking at a later age.
3. Women progress to problem drinking faster than men.
4. Women attribute the onset of drinking more often to life stressors or traumatic events.
5. More stigma is attached to female alcoholics.
6. Female alcoholics are more likely to have affective disorders, while males are more likely to have antisocial personalities.
7. Women feel greater consequences in their home lives, while men feel more in their jobs and careers.
8. Fewer drinking problems occur in husbands of alcoholic women than in wives of alcoholic men.
9. Women appear to experience more severe alcohol-related medical consequences than men.
10. Alcoholic women more often report feelings of anxiety, depression, and guilt than do their male counterparts.

Griffin, Weiss, Mirin, and Lange (1989) reported similar findings for female cocaine abusers. Compared to male cocaine abusers, they were more likely to have major depression and to experience residual problems such as job dissatisfaction when they were drug free. They were more likely to cite specific reasons for cocaine use, while men engaged in such drug use as part of an antisocial lifestyle. In contrast to findings with alcoholism, these women began cocaine use at an earlier age than men. Washton and Gold (1987) found that women were less likely than men to support their usage by drug dealing, but more likely to exchange sex for cocaine.

Several of these conclusions have notable implications for relapse prevention. First, the role of psychiatric disorders in relapse needs to be explored carefully. The possibility of self-medication and increased psychiatric severity seems to be increased for women. Second, the attributions that women make about the onset of their addictions may affect outcome. If stress-inducing circumstances are still present or if past traumas are not resolved, the risk of relapse may be increased. Third, the relative lack of social and occupational resources may preclude an improvement in environmental support for recovery. Women may experience fewer choices in changing their lifestyles. Fourth, women experience more stigma and shame because of negative stereotypes about their integrity, sexuality, and responsibility. The guilt that many women feel about issues such as child rearing can act as an obstacle to their recovery. In the following sections these biological, individual, and interpersonal differences are examined in detail.

Biological Difference from Men

Biological factors in relapse among women can be divided into three categories: (a) genetic, (b) medical, and (c) gynecological. The genetic basis of alcoholism in women is less well established than in men (Lex, 1985), but there is evidence that alcoholic women are more likely to have an alcoholic parent (especially the father) than are alcoholic men (Beckman, 1976). Combined with a concordance of about 25% for primary affective disorder (Schuckit, 1978), there seems to be at least a partial genetic factor at work.

Alcoholic women experience more medical consequences than alcoholic men. Diseases such as pancreatitis, cirrhosis, ulcers, and cardiovascular problems are more common in females (Bourne & Light, 1979) and may complicate their treatment progress. Alcoholic women report fewer blackouts, morning drinking episodes, and delirium tremens (Lex, 1985), but the total contribution of biological factors in their dependence remains unknown.

There have been anecdotal reports of links between drinking and hormonally disruptive events such as menopause, premenstrual tension, and childbirth (Lex, 1985). Hoard (1988) noted that during premenstrual periods, women may experience increased anxiety, insomnia, water retention, and mood swings in response to hormonal changes. Some women who experience premenstrual dysphoria are more likely to increase alcohol or marijuana use at premenstruum (Mello, 1986). Others may use alcohol as a diuretic or analgesic, but the relationship between alcohol use and premenstrual states is not simple (McCrady & Sher, 1983).

A useful technique is to question women on an individual basis as their coping styles may vary. Some may view menstrual discomfort as independent of drinking; others may self-medicate with alcohol or drugs. Perceptions of the usefulness of alcohol are probably more important than its actual utility. Many women attribute the onset of their drinking to gynecological problems such as dysmenorrhea, infertility, frequent miscarriages, or hysterectomy (Gomberg, 1980). However, Gomberg also reported that alcoholic drinking may occur long before events such as menopause.

Many female alcoholics that I have interviewed report that they were abstinent during pregnancy. Further questioning reveals the women were able to stop drinking and using drugs while they were pregnant but relapsed shortly after delivering their babies. Concerns about fetal alcohol syndrome are not lost on these women, but such concerns are often the *only* motivating factor. When they realize that their babies are healthy, they lose the major reason for abstaining. Postpartum relapse is also quite common among female smokers: 56% of women who stop smoking during pregnancy relapse within 30 days of delivery (McBride & Pirie, 1990). Many women use smoking as a way to lose weight after pregnancy. Relapse prevention may prove to be an effective intervention for women who have suspended use of a variety of substances during pregnancy.

Psychological Differences from Men

In addition to differences from males in affective disorders, female alcoholics report higher levels of guilt and anxiety with corresponding lower levels of self-esteem than do men (Tamerin, 1985). Sex-role conflict (involving dependency on men, lack of support systems, and lack of identity) is also frequently cited by women (Tamerin, 1985; Wilsnack, 1976). The prevailing negative stereotypes about female alcoholics and their tendency to report more life stresses make it likely that women will attribute their drinking to external causes (McCrady & Sher, 1983). Despite research indicating that programs segregating the sexes are no more effective than those combining them (Lex, 1985), therapists and counselors are still well advised to address issues of identity, sexuality, and independence as part of relapse prevention.

Social Differences from Men

Females are less likely to report vocational and legal problems but are more likely to report marital strife and hide their drinking from their friends and relatives (McCrady & Sher, 1983). These tendencies may enhance denial, as females may not easily focus on themselves. Hiding drinking or blaming it on an unsatisfying marriage does not allow feedback about the negative effects of drinking. As a result, a therapist may have more success discussing self-esteem, lack of self-growth, and lost family opportunities. These are especially important because women may face a more challenging reentry environment in the home. Husbands may not be as willing to sacrifice their time for the wife's recovery, and many do not even remain in the marriage. Alcoholic women are more likely to be divorced than alcoholic men, perhaps because of the social stigma assigned to the women (Lex, 1985).

For women who lose a significant other in early recovery, sex and dating can be extremely threatening. Many have never had sex or dated in a sober state. The possibility of isolation may be equally threatening, so addicted women need much guidance about ways to assess unhealthful relationships. Alcoholics Anonymous suggests "no relationships for the first year." There is nothing magical about this time span, although many treatment professionals recognize the dangers inherent in relationships in early recovery, especially if they arise out of "detox romances." Alcoholic women (and men) already in relationships should attempt to (a) establish separate treatment recovery programs to prevent a loss of attention to recovery, (b) diversify their social support to prevent dependency on their partner, and (c) be ready to detach from the relationship if their (or their partner's) personal growth is impeded.

THE ELDERLY

Despite findings that people drink less as they get older, there is still a significant alcoholism problem among the elderly (defined as people older than 55 or 65, depending upon the researcher). Nearly 1 in 5 uses alcohol frequently, while 1 in 10 admits to drinking heavily (Nowack, 1985). Zimberg (1985) suggests a 10% to 15% rate among the general population of elderly, with a higher rate among hospitalized elderly. In this latter group, approximately 20% to 25% are heavy drinkers or alcoholics (Blazer & Pennybacker, 1984). Alcoholism is the second most frequent reason for admission of elderly to psychiatric hospitals (Pursch, 1985). These figures are revealing, given society's preoccupation with substance abuse among adolescents and young adults. The number of elderly alcoholics will certainly grow as the proportion of older adults increases in the general population.

Elderly drug abuse is also likely to increase. People over 65 consume more than 25% of all prescription drugs (Green, 1978). There have been numerous reports of misuse and abuse of prescription drugs such as major and minor tranquilizers, antidepressants, hypnotics, and sedatives. Illegal drug use may exacerbate this problem. Although a relatively small proportion of individuals currently over 65 have used an illegal drug even once, the proportion of elderly drug addicts will likely rise as younger addicts age (Glantz, 1981). Increased availability of drugs should also be a contributing factor.

Biological Differences

The elderly are more likely than younger people to be dealing with physical illness and metabolic changes, which can potentiate the interaction between alcohol and prescribed medications, magnify the intoxicating effects of alcohol, or lower the immunity of organ systems to the effects of alcohol. The neuropsychological effects of alcohol, such as memory deficits, difficulties developing problem-solving strategies, and difficulties changing problem-solving strategies may be more severe in those with long-term alcoholic patterns (Miller & Saucedo, 1983). The elderly may have greater involvement with medical treatments, which might complicate and detract attention away from recovery. An elderly person who has succumbed to physical problems will likely deny his or her limitations; therefore, treatment professionals should expect acceptance of a substance abuse problem to be even more difficult to attain. Finally, recovery may prove excessively challenging even in the very motivated elderly person due to possible visual, hearing, and mobility problems.

Psychological Differences

When alcoholism has an early onset, there is a higher probability for psychopathology and medical complications (Zimberg, 1985). When alcoholism begins later in life, there is sometimes a greater association with life events such as bereavement, retirement, social isolation, physical impairments, or marital discord (Rosin & Glatt, 1971). Approximately two-thirds of the elderly alcoholics can be considered early onset, while one-third are late onset (Zimberg, 1985). Elderly alcoholics are more susceptible to falls, self-neglect, confusion, and querulous behaviors (Rosin & Glatt, 1971). Schuckit and Miller (1976) also found increased rates of suicide among elderly alcoholics. The combination of negative life events, neglect, multiple losses, and limited physical capacities can increase hopeless feelings, which in turn increase the risk of relapse.

Social Differences

Reduced income, retirement, restrictions in transportation (e.g., inability to drive), deaths of friends and relatives, and loss of recreational activities because of physical illness tend to limit the social support networks of elderly people. As discussed earlier, social support is a powerful predictor of relapse—and no segment of the population experiences such difficulties in developing healthy supports in early recovery.

The resulting social isolation and stigma among elderly alcoholics may lead to much "closet" drinking. This occurrence increases the risk of relapse and also makes initial identification of these alcoholics quite difficult. The shame of drinking or drug abuse may be especially acute among female elderly alcoholics. Unlike other populations, elderly alcoholics should probably be treated within substance-abuse treatment programs established specifically for the elderly rather than in alcoholism programs (Zimberg, 1985). This strategy allows greater socialization and involvement with population-specific recreational programs.

DUAL DIAGNOSIS PATIENTS

The population of dual diagnosis patients is forcing a rapprochement between psychiatric and substance abuse treatment. Dually diagnosed patients (those with diagnoses of both psychiatric problems and addiction) make up as much as 80% of substance abuse populations and 30% to 50% of psychiatric populations (Kosten & Kleber, 1988). From a relapse prevention standpoint, four issues are of primary importance: (a) denial that detracts attention away from sobriety, (b) self-medication, (c) fluctuation of psychiatric symptoms, and (d) timing of psychotherapy.

Denial

Dually diagnosed patients, particularly if they have been treated within the traditional mental health system, may have great difficulty in admitting and addressing their alcoholism and drug addiction. In many cases, their therapists have spent little time treating their substance abuse problems. The clinicians are sometimes unaware that there is a substance abuse problem at all. Under these conditions, progress in treating the substance abuse problem (and usually the psychiatric problem) is stalled. Relapses can be frequent and will continue if both disorders are not treated concurrently. Convincing patients that dual disorders have mutual effects is central to breaking denial. I have found that many patients respond to the analogy that they have to remain on "both tracks" to prevent "derailing" in treatment. Abstinence becomes a prerequisite to addressing the psychiatric disorder successfully.

Self-Medication

The most obvious reason for substance abuse in a dually diagnosed patient is to medicate the psychiatric disorder. Panic sufferers often abuse alcohol (Hudson & Perkins, 1984) or benzodiazepines such as

Valium or Xanax (Allgulander, Borg, & Vikander, 1984). Depressed patients may use cocaine to neutralize psychomotor slowing and low energy levels (Cohen, 1987). They have also been known to abuse alcohol for its initial stimulatory effects (Goodwin, 1988). Schizophrenics may abuse hallucinogens or stimulants to relieve dysphoria or counteract negative symptoms such as attentional impairment, emotional flattening, asocial behavior, or anhedonia (Schneier & Siris, 1987). There are indications that individuals with bipolar disorder may use alcohol (Solomon, 1989) or cocaine (Kleber & Gawin, 1987). These tendencies make it absolutely essential to evaluate carefully the need for medication, particularly those medicines with cross-addictive potential. This action is particularly important for patients receiving psychiatric medications with potential for abuse (e.g., benzodiazepines for treating anxiety disorders). If possible, medications with less abusive potential should be used or alternative methods such as relaxation training should be considered.

Fluctuation of Psychiatric Symptoms

In early recovery, alcohol and drug withdrawal mimic a variety of psychiatric disorders. Most substance abusers will meet the criteria for some psychiatric disorder. As recovery progresses, most of these symptoms abate. As many as two-thirds of hospitalized male alcoholics report psychiatric symptoms in addition to alcoholism (Penick, Powell, Liskow, Jackson, & Nickel, 1988). The stability of these symptoms varies, depending on the particular psychiatric disorder. Penick and his colleagues found that drug abuse, antisocial personality, and depression were reasonably stable over a 1-year period. The identification of mania and anxiety disorders was less reliable. Brown and Schuckit (1988) found that mood-related symptoms of depression abated fairly rapidly, but that vegetative symptoms were often prevalent at discharge.

The initial presentation is affected by the abused substance(s), so clinical decision making can be quite complex. There should be a monitoring period beyond detoxification which will vary in length depending on the patient's psychiatric history, detoxification history, past medications used, psychosocial stressors, and self-report validity. This period should be for at least 1 to 2 weeks after detoxification (Kaufman, 1989). When these symptoms become severe, the possibility of suicidal ideation must be a major concern. Alcoholic suicide attempters more often have multiple psychiatric diagnoses and severe symptoms than nonattempters (Hesselbrock, Hesselbrock, Syzmanski, & Weidenman, 1988). In such cases, aggressive psychopharmacological treatment may be required so that the patient can focus on treatment.

Timing of Psychotherapy

Because of the concrete demands of early recovery, there has been much speculation in the literature about whether or when insight-oriented psychotherapy should be introduced among alcoholics and drug addicts (Bean-Bayog, 1985; Kaufman, 1989). For dually diagnosed people, great care should be exercised with this method.

Bean-Bayog (1985) divides psychotherapy for addicted individuals into three phases: (a) achieving sobriety, (b) maintaining abstinence and early recovery, and (c) advanced recovery. The second phase, which represents relapse prevention, involves supportive forms of psychotherapy that assist the patient in avoiding drug substitution, unhealthful relationships, and defenses such as rationalization and denial. Advanced recovery involves reconstructive work aimed at exploring underlying issues such as family trauma, lack of identity, and intimacy.

The last phase, which may take 2 years to reach, would probably address deep-seated family issues. Therapists are well advised to avoid these issues early in treatment as they require intensive intervention and focus by the patient. Introducing them too early may shake the already unstable emotional foundations of patients in early recovery and precipitate a relapse. It is best to develop a stable foundation of emotional support and to help the patient improve coping skills before delving into vague and confusing emotions engendered by an alcoholic family. For dual diagnosis patients with primitive defensive structures (e.g., schizophrenics), insight-oriented approaches may be contraindicated (Kaufman, 1989). Indeed, the main thrust in the treatment of dual diagnosis patients in early recovery should be simply to keep them in treatment. They tend to have the highest dropout rate among the subgroups of substance abusers (Rounsaville, Weissman, Kleber & Wilber, 1982).

IMPAIRED PROFESSIONALS

Treatment professionals are becoming increasingly aware of the presence of alcoholism and drug addiction within their own ranks. There is a growing literature documenting addiction among physicians (Talbott & Martin, 1984), nurses (Isler, 1978), psychologists (Laliotis & Grayson, 1985), and counselors (Kinney, 1983). Experts estimate that as many as 200,000 nurses may be chemically dependent (Diamant, 1989) and that the rate of narcotics addiction among physicians is 30 to 100 times greater than it is within the general population (Jefferson & Ensor, 1982). Among psychologists, at least 6,000 Ph.D.s can be considered alcoholic (Thoresen, Nathan, Skorina, & Kilburg, 1983). Within the substance abuse treatment field, many professionals are themselves recovering alcoholics and addicts.

Relapse within this population could be destructive and potentially life threatening for both the professional and the patient.

These professionals present special problems for relapse prevention. First, because they ostensibly represent an image of competence and strength to their patients, they may have difficulty admitting the insecurities associated with relapse. This is nowhere more evident than in the social perceptions about physicians, who are often expected to be infallible. In an effort to project an image of self-control, many practitioners may suppress their feelings and avoid discussion of their shame and disappointments.

Second, treatment professionals view themselves as helpers rather than "helpees." When receiving psychotherapy and counseling, they need to suspend judgment about how they are being treated and avoid rationalization. They need to be more responsive to supervision. It is quite natural for impaired professionals to assume the role of observer, but the clinician should be quick to point out that the professional patient need not "study" treatment in order to feel its effects, nor does knowledge guarantee sobriety.

Third, professionals tend to be mutually protective, which can worsen denial. The feedback essential to relapse prevention can be lacking, especially as many impaired professionals can continue to function in a marginally acceptable way while actively abusing substances (Thoresen et al., 1983). In many cases, their performance is bolstered by well-meaning colleagues. In early recovery, addicted professionals often try to compensate for past below par performances by engaging in workaholic patterns. This approach perpetuates one-dimensional views of self-worth and unbalanced lifestyles. Fortunately, many professional associations provide advocacy and support for colleagues in early recovery.

Finally, many health care professionals reenter work environments that force them to have contact with potentially addicting substances. For physicians and nurses dispensing medications, cue reactivity is a daily threat. As part of relapse prevention, the patients need to evaluate these cues and develop coping strategies (e.g., avoidance, change in responsibilities, or social support).

Chapter 8

Relapse Prevention with Substitute Addictions

The two biggest sellers in any bookstore are the
cookbooks and the diet books. The cookbooks tell
you how to prepare the food and the diet books
tell you how not to eat any of it.

—*Andy Rooney*

With all the contradictory information about substance use in our society, it is no surprise that alcoholics and addicts are highly vulnerable to other addictions. Abstaining from one's addiction of choice is only half the battle. A recent national study of treatment effectiveness with 10,000 drug addicts of various types found that despite significant reductions in regular use of their preferred drug, there was relatively little change in regular alcohol or marijuana use over a 5-year follow-up period (Hubbard et al., 1989). Rather than develop new and healthful coping styles, many alcoholics and addicts use an alternative substance to relieve physical and emotional pain (Gorski & Miller, 1986).

These substitutions are not limited to drugs. In my own assessment of 100 relapsed alcoholics and drug addicts, I found that only 29% did *not* substitute some alternative addiction (Chiauzzi, 1990). These alternatives included gambling, compulsive eating, nicotine abuse, caffeine abuse, workaholism, dependency on relationships, and compulsive spending. Forty-eight percent reported at least two substitutions. There was a significant difference in average number of substitutions between alcoholics (1.4) and drug addicts (2.3).

This chapter is a review of clinical considerations for particular compulsive behaviors that many consider addictions. Behaviors become addictive if they meet three criteria: (a) loss of control, (b) need or compulsion, and (c) continued use despite adverse consequences (Gold, Washton, & Dackis, 1985). Loss of control is characterized by inability to refuse opportunities to perform the activity as well as alteration of daily patterns to accommodate the activity. Need or compulsion arises when an individual is preoccupied with the activity or becomes irritable when unable to perform it. Continued use despite adverse consequences is perhaps the most important feature: The individual remains engaged in the activity with the knowledge that he or she will regret it later. The cardinal features of activities that become compulsive are that they are relied on as the primary form of coping and are not voluntarily moderated.

Each substitute addiction can increase the potential for relapse. Because particular behaviors (e.g., working, spending, or cigarette smoking) are so common among members of the general population, they may be unwittingly regarded as safe by individuals at risk for relapse. The following discussion provides evidence for the special risks of these behaviors in recovering people.

NICOTINE ADDICTION

The smoke-free philosophy prevalent in most of society has eluded substance abusers, but they should pay attention to it. Evidence suggests that the continuation of smoking in recovery from other addictive substances represents a risk factor for relapse. Over 90% of alcoholics are cigarette smokers (Istvan & Matarazzo, 1984), compared to roughly 30% in the general population (Pierce, Fiore, Novotny, Hatziandreu, & Davis, 1989). A high proportion of alcoholics (between one-quarter and one-third) are heavy smokers, defined as 40+ cigarettes per day (Istvan & Matarazzo, 1984).

Heavy drinkers are less likely to attempt to stop smoking (Zimmerman, Warheit, Ulbrich, & Auth, 1990). Only 7% of alcoholic smokers who *do* try to stop are successful, compared to 49% of nonalcoholic smokers (DiFranza & Guerrera, 1990). These findings suggest that smoking is not merely a bad habit, but is a manifestation of underlying addictive tendencies in alcoholics.

As smoking increasingly becomes regarded as a deviant activity, it is probable that the lighter smokers will quit, leaving a core of severely addicted smokers. This group manifests greater addictive tendencies, poorer health habits, and more antisocial behavior than the general population (Coambs, Kozlowski, & Ferrence, 1989). These characteristics will further isolate smokers and society may subsequently regard them as they now regard alcoholics and drug addicts.

Despite strong public health warnings, the presence of caffeine and nicotine at Alcoholics Anonymous meetings can imply to the recovering alcoholic that such behaviors are endorsed by members of the organization. This assumption is risky, given that at least 300,000 people die from tobacco-related problems each year (U.S. Public Health Service, 1989). This death rate is greater than that for all other drugs combined (Shaffer & Jones, 1989).

Most substance abuse treatment programs subscribe to the traditional philosophy that addressing nicotine addiction in the early phases of recovery can drive patients away and increase the risk of relapse. This approach contradicts the philosophy of A.A. itself that "a drug is a drug." Despite claims that negative outcomes would result, a recent survey by the American Society of Addiction Medicine found relatively few complaints in programs with no-smoking policies (Hurt & Slade, 1990). Half of the 214 treatment center directors did not believe that if their patients stopped smoking it would interfere with their recovery from drugs and alcohol. In addition, their review of smoking cessation among psychiatric patients indicated that even those with severe mental illness were able to quit. No-smoking policies tend *not* to increase the number of patients who leave against medical advice, to lower occupancy rates, or to require increased physical restraints. Much of the resistance comes from treatment staff, many of whom are recovering themselves but are still actively smoking.

Recovering addicts' ambivalence about stopping nicotine use may be related to their awareness of its addictive potential. Recent surveys suggest that many drug addicts view smoking as the most difficult habit to "kick." Lynn Kozlowski of the Addiction Research Foundation in Toronto conducted three surveys (reported in "Drug Addicts," 1990). The first survey showed that 57% considered cigarettes harder than other drugs to give up. The second survey reported that 33% felt stronger urges for cigarettes than for their drug of choice. The third survey reported that alcoholics and cocaine users experienced greater urges and less pleasure with cigarettes than with other drugs. There was a strong link between nicotine use and the number of other drugs used. Seventy-five percent of single-drug users were smokers, but 100% of those using six drugs were smokers.

There are other indications that smoking, especially for substance abusers, does not exist in a vacuum. Recent surveys show that heavy smokers drink more, are less active physically, and are more likely to sleep less than nonsmokers ("Smokers' Problems," 1988). The same article reported that smokers more often use medications, get into arguments, and engage in risky behavior such as visiting high-crime areas and carrying weapons.

Taken together, the strong relationship between smoking and substance abuse, the tolerance of smoking within self-help and treatment settings, the perception among alcoholics and addicts that nicotine addiction is more powerful than addiction to other drugs, and the connection between smoking and unhealthful lifestyles suggests that smoking can be a significant risk factor in recovery. In the interest of treatment consistency and the promotion of healthful habits, alcoholics and drug addicts should be treated simultaneously for nicotine addiction. Because they seem to have greater difficulty quitting than the general population, formal behavioral, cognitive, medical, and educational interventions need to be incorporated into traditional substance abuse treatment. The abstinence approach is strongly indicated—smokers who quit "cold turkey" are more likely to remain abstinent than those who attempt to taper off through lower daily consumption, lower tar cigarettes, or special filters (Fiore et al., 1990).

COCAINE ADDICTION

No drug has received more attention in recent years than cocaine. Several characteristics associated with cocaine pose special problems for relapse prevention: (a) mystique, (b) binge patterns, (c) polydrug usage, (d) narcissistic indulgence, (e) a lack of a significant withdrawal effect, and (f) powerful cue reactivity.

Cocaine has its own unique mythology that functions to minimize the negative effects of the drug. Addicts frequently deny their problem with comments such as "Everybody is doing it," "It helps me with depression," "It makes relationships more interesting," "It helps me with my sex life," or "I only snort it."

Each of these perceptions can be disproven by examining the experience of most cocaine addicts. Cocaine is certainly not abused by everyone since 25 million people have tried it and only 2.5% to 5% of these users can be considered addicted (Shaffer & Jones, 1989). Cocaine's antidepressant qualities are questionable since its short-term euphoria can lead to dysphoria (and for some, suicide). Cocaine may make relationships and sex appear better, but most cocaine addicts report a severe deterioration in the quality of their social and sex lives over time and with continued use (Gold, 1990). Some may regard snorting as safe, but the experience of the 800-CO-CAINE hotline warns that it can result in seizures (Gold, 1990). Those who graduate to freebasing or intravenous use cannot be considered casual users, considering the risks, cost, and drug effects involved.

Cocaine is by nature a binge drug (Dupont, 1987). Users may report that they use it only once a week or once a month, but they neglect to say that these instances last for days at a time, often with little or no sleep. The intermittent abstinent periods may give the user the impression of control, but probably they just represent a lack of money, serious consequences from the last binge, or lack of availability of cocaine. During these periods, there is no real recovery going on, but simply a prelude to the next binge.

Cocaine tends to be used as part of a polydrug pattern. Many users progress from alcohol, discovering that they can drink more under the influence of cocaine. Others develop new addictions in an effort to neutralize the effects of cocaine. Because cocaine can be quite energizing and create edgy, irritable, and paranoid reactions, many people combine it with alcohol, tranquilizer, or opiate use. When treated, cocaine addicts often deny these other addictions by rationalizing that they would abstain from the other drugs by virtue of stopping cocaine. Further questioning usually reveals that these other drugs now stand on their own and should be treated as primary addictions. Cocaine is particularly troubling because it is also introducing intravenous usage to those who typically have "needle phobias." As a result, many cocaine users are now faced with the threat of AIDS or hepatitis.

Cocaine has been considered a "rich man's drug" and has led many users to feel as if it conferred a high-status image on them. The euphoria of cocaine can give users the sense that they can accomplish anything. Many users feel like "Superman" under its influence. These effects have been supported by a societal philosophy of "pleasure now, pay later" (Cohen, 1987). In actuality, these perceptions are very different from reality, as many addicts live in squalor and support themselves through "hustling" money from their friends and acquaintances. When these people appear for treatment, they have difficulty breaking through the misconceptions. Relapse prevention should address issues of self-efficacy and help the addict develop lifestyle changes that improve self-esteem.

Cocaine does not have the severe physical withdrawal effects of drugs such as alcohol, benzodiazepines, nicotine, or heroin. Despite claims in the media, cocaine tends to be associated with *fewer* medical problems and deaths than alcohol (Washton, 1989). Cocaine addicts tend not to require supervised inpatient detoxification to manage withdrawal. The most notable features of cocaine withdrawal are psychological—prolonged sleep, depressed mood, and fatigue (Siegel, 1987). As medical problems are a primary motivator for many people, cocaine addicts may have a lower likelihood of seeking treatment. Once in treatment, many cocaine users feel as if they are back to normal, a sensation that creates an illusion of well-being. Some may feel so committed to recovery that their cravings diminish, but there tends to be a recurrence about 2 weeks into recovery (Gawin & Kleber, 1986). At this point, addicts are especially vulnerable to relapse and should be educated about the cycle of cocaine withdrawal effects.

The cue reactivity generated by cocaine is perhaps more powerful than that of any other drug. My discussions with cocaine addicts have been quite illuminating, as it appears that just about anything white can set off an urge. Cocaine addicts report that everyday items such salt, artificial sweetener, shaving cream, and ashes from cigarettes reminded them of cocaine. Soda bottles, tin foil, and baking soda (used in freebasing) remind addicts of "the pipe." Credit cards and driver's licenses often trigger thoughts of cocaine because they are used to cut it. The graphic drug scenes that frequently turn up in television programs lead many users to feel high. Because cocaine use is dependent on the availability of large amounts of money, many addicts relapse when they receive their first paycheck. As mentioned in chapter 5, a careful and complete analysis of drug cues is essential for relapse prevention.

EATING DISORDERS

Many researchers and clinicians consider compulsive overeating and bulimia to be addictions (Yeary & Heck, 1989; Wooley & Wooley, 1981). The incidence of compulsive overeating in recovering people is unclear, but it is probably more common than bulimia (Yeary & Heck, 1989). There is a sex difference in the disorders, as about 90% of bulimics are women (Striegel-Moore, Silberstein, & Rodin, 1986). The prevalence rate for this disorder is 1% among adolescent and young adult women (Fairburn & Beglin, 1990). These women appear especially vulnerable to societal expectations about attractiveness, thinness, and fitness.

The major symptoms exhibited by compulsive overeaters are reminiscent of the conflicted thoughts and behaviors seen in substance-addicted people. Compulsive overeaters experience (a) binge eating with an awareness that the pattern is abnormal, (b) fear of not being able to stop eating voluntarily, (c) depressed mood, and (d) self-deprecating thoughts following binges (Siegal, Brisman, & Weinshel, 1988).

Bulimia is characterized by similar patterns of overeating. Approximately 50% of bulimics binge daily (Johnson, Stuckey, Lewis, & Schwartz, 1982). These episodes are usually precipitated by anxiety and negative emotional states, but the overeating does not usually alleviate these feelings (Weiss, Katzman, & Wolchick, 1985). The bulimic typically consumes foods that are highly caloric and require little preparation (e.g., sweets and fast foods).

Second, bulimics tend to engage in extreme behaviors designed to control weight. They go on crash diets, exercise excessively, or use large amounts of laxatives or diuretics. What separates bulimics from overeaters is that 80% to 90% induce vomiting; approximately 50% do this daily (Weiss et al., 1985). Fifty percent abuse laxatives and half of this group does it daily (Johnson et al., 1982).

Third, bulimics are extremely concerned about their shape and weight. They tend to exaggerate their body size, overidealize thinness, and experience low self-esteem with regard to their body image (Striegel-Moore et al., 1986). As in other addictions, bulimia is considered a lifelong psychological and physical battle.

There is increasing evidence that eating disorders and substance abuse are related. Bulimics have a higher prevalence of substance abuse (Hat-sukami, Eckert, Mitchell, & Pyle, 1984). In a recent study, 22% of cocaine abusers calling the 800-COCAINE hotline met the DSM-III criteria for bulimia (Jonas, Gold, Sweeney, & Pottash, 1987). There is an increased family incidence of alcohol and drug abuse in individuals diagnosed with eating disorders (Bulik, 1987).

Available evidence indicates that compulsive overeating and bulimia share many characteristics with substance abuse (Brisman & Siegel, 1984; Wooley & Wooley, 1981). The disorder is often kept secret. It shows a progression from adolescent concerns about weight to discovery of self-induced vomiting to loss of control in unsupervised environments (typi-cally college). People with eating disorders report strong preoccupations with food and a distortion in lifestyle to support their eating patterns. Many become privately disturbed about their eating and try (unsuccess-fully) to change the destructive pattern. They often relapse when they begin to gain weight or experience food cravings. They engage in obses-sive-compulsive behavior, which is supported by "all-or-none" and per-fectionistic thinking. Particularly among young recovering women, these behaviors and cognitions may apply equally to substances that they are abusing. In early recovery, they may use binge eating as a replacement for their drug of choice. An active eating disorder may increase the risk of relapse since it precludes more healthful coping methods.

While it is tempting to equate eating disorders and substance abuse, there is disagreement among professionals about how closely these dis-orders correlate. For instance, bulimics with substance abuse problems resemble substance abusers more than they resemble bulimics without substance abuse problems (Shisslak et al., 1989). In addition, some treat-ment professionals suggest that women may find it productive to consider their eating disorders within the context of a 12-step program (i.e., identi-fying themselves with a lifelong eating disorder) (Yeary & Heck, 1989). However, there is a lack of empirical data supporting the efficacy of self-help approaches (Mitchell, Hoberman, & Pyle, 1989).

Traditional eating disorder programs (those that focus on psychother-apy rather than an addiction philosophy) stress the importance of forming an identity *apart* from the eating disorder, and they do not regard such disorders as lifelong. Professionals using this approach report low recidi-vism (Shisslak, Schnaps, & Crago, 1989), but they tend not to use absti-nence as a criterion.

COMPULSIVE GAMBLING

Gambling is becoming an increasingly available social activity, ranging from state lotteries to casino gambling to illegal sports betting. Approximately 1% to 3% of the adult population in the United States experiences significant gambling problems (Commission on the Review of the National Policy Towards Gambling, 1976). The risk of compulsive gambling rises dramatically with alcoholics and drug addicts. One study found that 5% of alcoholics and 12% of those with mixed alcohol and drug dependence met the criteria for compulsive gambling (Lesieur, Blume, & Zoppa, 1986). Research also shows that histories of parental pathological gambling and paternal alcoholism were associated with higher rates of compulsive gambling in the children (Lesieur et al., 1986; Ramirez, McCormick, Russo, & Taber, 1984). The linkage between compulsive gambling and substance abuse is also evident in clinical observations of alcoholics and drug addicts who replace substances with gambling (Blume & Lesieur, 1988).

Gambling is considered a high-stimulation activity that may fulfill sensation seeking needs for some individuals (Custer & Milt, 1985). Compulsive gamblers may reach an optimum level of arousal when betting, which may produce a narrowing of attention, disordered thinking, and sometimes confusional states (Brown, 1986). These cognitive states may provide an escape from reality, which may be perceived as rewarding. However, the nature of gambling is that these rewards are variable, making compulsive gambling difficult to stop. The intensity of these effects may have a basis in biological abnormalities in the noradrenergic (Roy et al., 1988) or endorphin (Blaszcynski, Winter, & McConaghy, 1986) systems.

In the absence of healthy stimulating alternatives, the sensation-seeking substance abuser in early recovery will be at particular risk for compulsive gambling. The risk of compulsive gambling increases as the number of drugs abused increases. As addicted individuals resolve problems and stabilize daily patterns, they may experience an inability to tolerate a lack of conflict (typically associated with states of excitation). The excitement that once came so easily may become so elusive that the addict may try to retain one last addiction. In my experience, substance-addicted gamblers hide their gambling even while they are actively (and often successfully) addressing their alcohol and drug use. Education about the dangers of substitution and healthy stimulating alternatives can provide the reassurance needed to lower the risk of relapse.

EXCESSIVE WORK

The moral model of addiction has given rise to many myths suggesting the characterological inferiority of alcoholics, particularly with regard to their work ethic. There is no evidence that alcoholics and addicts are less hard working than any other subgroup. In fact, many are *more* motivated to work hard so that they can support their addictions. Excessive work can also function as a substitute for the abused substance, with the assumption that time accounted for is time that cannot be devoted to substance use. Apart from the fact that excessive work interferes with aftercare compliance, fatigue and boredom can take a psychological toll.

The behavior of alcoholics and addicts who take a workaholic approach to recovery is reminiscent of the Type A personality characteristics described by Friedman and Ulmer (1984). According to these authors, coronary-prone individuals experience time urgency, free-floating hostility, and a self-destructive tendency.

My discussions with relapsed alcoholics and addicts showed clearly that manifestation of these qualities often preceded relapse. Many of these people compulsively fill their schedules with work and household tasks in an attempt to avoid any inactive or solitary time. The amount done becomes more important than the quality of the work. When these actions are taken to an extreme, they often are associated by the patients with an almost slavish devotion to the clock.

The resulting pressures can increase stress and lead to complaining, critical comments, profanity, and aggressive behavior. These behaviors may not be associated with specific situations and may be triggered by relatively insignificant events. Alcoholics Anonymous members refer to these behaviors as a "dry drunk."

Self-destructive behavior does not necessarily imply suicidal tendencies. Less obvious reactions such as overeating, poor exercise habits, or inconsistent sleep patterns are more likely. Alcoholics or addicts may show a lack of self-care in response to excessive work. They may regard their material accomplishments as more important than their physical integrity.

Maladaptive work habits are frequent in compulsive personalities. In accordance with the organization valued by these people, work provides an objective means with a definite beginning and end by which they can measure themselves. Emotions and subjectivity tend to be devalued because they interfere with productivity. These people live a one-dimensional life, defining their identities in hours worked, salary earned, or approval given by peers. They may not feel alive unless they are on the job; consequently, their relationships suffer. Issues of control, self-centeredness, and rigidity intrude on balanced living.

Addicted individuals who substitute work for their drug of choice need to be supported in developing alternative coping styles. They should be encouraged to include *noncompetitive* leisure activities in their daily schedules, especially those that involve other people. Myths of workaholism also need to be addressed (e.g., that workaholics are invariably productive; they may simply be inefficient). Most important, the therapist needs to realize that compulsive work is an ego-syntonic condition—the alcoholic or addict may perceive it not as a problem but as a desirable way of living. If the clinician simply suggests a revamped work style, the patient will probably respond with much resistance and noncompliance. Building on the workaholic's devotion to schedules and organization by including a broader range of recovery-oriented activities (A.A., exercise, spirituality, and family recreation), the therapist can create a more favorable climate for change.

OTHER COMPULSIVE BEHAVIORS

Addictive behavior need not be limited to the "isms." Some behaviors are considered healthy in moderation but may become pathological if abused. Three behaviors that may be "quietly" abused are sex, spending, and exercise. With each of these, compulsiveness may not be readily noticed or assessed. Recovering people are not typically asked by their peers about their sexual behavior, spending habits, or exercise patterns. However, I have treated relapsers whose excessive involvement in these activities was unnoticed prior to their relapses. Psychologically, the relapser may come to rely upon such behaviors to act as antidepressants, escapes, or releases.

Sexual behavior and relationships are subject to the same abusive potential as alcohol and drugs. Dependence on a love object is the main form of coping; this is accompanied by a lack of self-confidence and fears of rejection. Milkman and Sunderwirth (1987) suggest that denial, progression, and withdrawal can also be found in sexual and romantic relationships. The compulsive individual will often deny the presence of a negative relationship, progress through the relationship in a downward spiral, and experience emotional and physical reactions when separated from the love object. Even in obviously abusive relationships, the "addicted" individual will focus on rare positive interactions, similar to the euphoric recall of drug effects.

Compulsive sexual behavior is prominent among cocaine abusers and may contribute to their relapse (Washton, 1989). Cocaine may produce hypersexuality in the form of sexual binges (unusually frequent sex, compulsive masturbation, or multiple partners), bizarre sexual fantasies, use of pornography, uncharacteristic sexual behavior (e.g., homosexuality in a heterosexual individual), or the use of sex to obtain cocaine (Washton & Stone-Washton, 1990). These behaviors are more likely to occur among males and cocaine smokers (Washton, 1989). After the drug use is discontinued, the feelings of shame and embarrassment associated with the sexual activity may not disappear. The clinician will need to help the patient distinguish between healthy and compulsive uses of sex and to explore the connection between sexual issues and triggers for relapse.

Developing new relationships in early recovery also poses a threat to many alcoholics and addicts. "All-or-none" thinking can create an obsession with the love object, interfering with recovery. Many patients have never been involved in sober sexual interactions. The angry emotions that can be aroused in relationships can bring back memories of past emotional trauma. Opportunities for new sober experiences can be subverted by pressures to focus energies on the relationship. If the new partner is also recovering, the social support he or she can offer may be tenuous and inconsistent because of the partner's own emotional struggles.

Compulsive spending is another common activity that can keep addictive tendencies alive. With the easy availability of consumer credit, bank teller cards, and checking accounts, there is a strong temptation for some recovering individuals to seek escape through materialism. Compulsive spenders may experience intense arousal followed by satiation, then depression and remorse (Milkman & Sunderwirth, 1987). Like substance addictions, compulsive spending may result in irrational judgments, such as buying expensive items or using purchases to ameliorate depression and feelings of emptiness. Some compulsive spenders do not even open the items they buy. Money may be diverted from legitimate expenses such as rent or food.

The ubiquity of compulsive spending has led to the formation of a self-help organization in San Francisco known as Spendermenders. This organization emphasizes the role of spending as a tranquilizer and a source of feeling alive (*Spendermenders,* 1986). Its literature suggests that compulsive spenders are preoccupied with money and that they are obsessed by having to spend it quickly. These individuals rely on money and possessions as a way of gaining identities without exploring underlying emotional issues such as fear, insecurity, and low self-esteem. Such patterns are reminiscent of the expectancies that alcoholics and drug addicts have of their substances.

One recovering alcoholic with whom I worked reported that he "discovered" credit cards during 1 year of abstinence (and A.A. attendance). He accumulated $16,000 in debt without even mentioning it to his A.A. sponsor. His financial problems caught up with him and he eventually relapsed on heroin. He later realized that his compulsiveness had never stopped and that he was at risk for relapse as long as he ignored it. At best, quick fixes in recovery provide only short-lived coping with emotional pain.

Compulsive exercise provides yet another avenue toward relapse for the recovering alcoholic or addict. Such individuals are often perfectionistic, competitive, and driven in their desires to achieve good health (Zaitz, 1989). Some engage in aerobics, weight lifting, or running even when they are injured or physically ill. They may be preoccupied with exercise or experience negative emotional reactions such as irritability, anxiety, or guilt if they miss a workout. I have seen several recovering alcoholics relapse after they injured themselves following a period of compulsive running. Their inactivity left them bereft of a sense of purpose and the void was eventually filled with a substance.

WHAT ABOUT THE LONG RUN?

As time passes, those who are successful in early recovery may find that they frequently ask themselves, "Is this all there is?" This question may first appear 6, 9, or 12 months into recovery. Recovering alcoholics and addicts sometimes feel as if they must join self-help groups for each problem that arises. They may also regard the future with trepidation, as they often suspect enjoyable activities of being possible addictions.

Two main points need to be considered. First, the issues of early recovery are quite different from issues in later recovery. When a person becomes abstinent, there is a need to focus on simple cognitive and behavioral changes. Over time, the complexity of changes needed in life increases while the pace of change decreases. The recovering person's concerns frequently turn from ways of stopping drug use to ways of improving the quality of life. Emotional, spiritual, and philosophical questions may arise: "What am I going to do with my life?" "How do I get to know myself better?" "How am I going to get meaning into my life?" It is important for the clinician to assure the patient that these questions are a natural outgrowth of the recovery process. However, their answers will be less concrete and less obvious than those for the questions asked in early recovery.

Second, Zackon (1988) suggests that relapse prevention necessarily involves training patients in "re-joyment." The satisfaction that recovering people feel for abstinence can sustain them for only so long; they must develop activities that create joy because the initial glow of recovery wears off in the absence of joyful activities. As Zackon states, "If addiction was hell, at least it was a familiar hell; abstinence ushers in new devils" (1988, p. 72). The task of relapse prevention is to convince the addict or alcoholic that these new devils can be mastered. The happiness of a new life will be harder to gain but it will be more enduring.

References

Abbott, M. W., & Gregson, R. A. M. (1981). Cognitive dysfunction in the prediction of relapse in alcoholism. *Journal of Studies on Alcohol, 43,* 230–243.

Abrams, D. B., Monti, P. M., Pinto, R. P., Elder, J. P., Brown, R. A., & Jacobus, S. I. (1987). Psychosocial stress and coping in smokers who relapse or quit. *Health Psychology, 6,* 289–303.

Addictive personality: "No such thing." (1990, April). *Clinical Psychiatry News,* p. 4.

Ahles, T. A., Schlundt, D. G., Prue, D. M., & Rychtarik, R. G. (1983). Impact of aftercare arrangements on the maintenance of treatment success in abusive drinkers. *Addictive Behaviors, 8,* 53–58.

Alcohol and cognitive loss. (1984, September). *National Clearinghouse for Alcohol Information Special Supplement,* pp. 1A–4A.

Allgulander, C., Borg, S., & Vikander, B. (1984). A 4–6-year follow-up of 50 patients with primary dependence on sedative and hypnotic drugs. *American Journal of Psychiatry, 141,* 1580–1582.

Annis, H. M. (1982). *Inventory of Drinking Situations.* Toronto, Canada: Addiction Research Foundation.

Annis, H. M. (1986). A relapse prevention model for treatment of alcoholics. In W. R. Miller & N. Heather (Eds.), *Treating addictive behaviors: Processes of change* (pp. 407–433). New York: Plenum Press.

Annis, H. M. (1987). *Situational Confidence Questionnaire.* Toronto, Canada: Addiction Research Foundation.

Annis, H. M., & Davis, C. S. (1989). Relapse prevention. In R. K. Hester & W. R. Miller (Eds.), *Handbook of alcoholism treatment approaches* (pp. 170–182). Elmsford, NY: Pergamon Press.

Armor, D. J., Polich, J. M., & Stambul, H. B. (1978). *Alcoholism and treatment.* New York: John Wiley & Sons.

Army Individual Test. (1944). Manual of directions and scoring. Washington, DC: War Department, Adjutant General's Office.

Babor, T. F., & Lauerman, R. J. (1986) Classification and forms in inebriety: Historical antecedents of alcoholic typologies. *Recent Development in Alcohol, 4,* 113–144.

Baekland, F. (1977). Evaluation of treatment methods in chronic alcoholism. In B. Kissin & H. Begleiter (Eds.), *The biology of alcoholism. Vol. IV. Treatment and rehabilitation of the chronic alcoholic* (pp. 385–440). New York: Plenum Press.

Baekland, F., & Lundwall, L. (1975). Dropping out of treatment: A critical review. *Psychological Bulletin, 5,* 738–783.

Baekland, F., Lundwall, L., & Kissin, B. (1975). Methods for the treatment of chronic alcoholism: A critical appraisal. In J. G. Gibbons, Y. Israel, H. Kalant, R. E. Popham, W. Schmidt, & R. G. Smart (Eds.), *Research advances in alcohol and drug problems* (Vol. 2, pp. 247–327). New York: John Wiley & Sons.

Baer, J. S., & Lichtenstein, E. (1988). Classification and prediction of smoking relapse episodes: An exploration of individual differences. *Journal of Consulting and Clinical Psychology, 56,* 104–110.

Bandura, A. (1977). *Social learning theory.* Englewood Cliffs, NJ: Prentice-Hall.

Bean-Bayog, M. (1985, March). *Psychotherapy and the sober alcoholic.* Paper presented at the Eighth Annual Alcoholism Symposium: Strategies and Objectives for Treatment Interventions, Boston, MA.

Beck, A., Ward, C., Mendelson, M., Mock, J., & Erbaugh, J. (1961). An inventory for measuring depression. *Archives of General Psychiatry, 4,* 561–571.

Becker, J. T., & Jaffe, J. H. (1984). Impaired memory for treatment relevant information in inpatient men alcoholics. *Journal of Studies on Alcohol, 45,* 339–343.

Beckman, L. J., (1976). Alcoholism problems and women: An overview. In M. Greenblatt & M. A. Schuckit (Eds.), *Alcoholism problems in women and children* (pp. 65–96). New York: Grune & Stratton.

Begleiter, H., Porjesz, B., Bihari, B., & Kissin, B. (1984). Event-related brain potentials in boys at high risk for alcoholism. *Science, 225,* 1493–1496.

Beitman, B. D., Goldfried, M. R., & Norcross, J. C. (1989). The movement toward integrating the psychotherapies: An overview. *American Journal of Psychiatry, 146,* 138–147.

Bellack, A. S., Hersen, M., & Himmelhoch, J. M. (1978). *Social skills training for depression: A treatment manual.* Washington, DC: JSAS Catalog of Selected Documents in Psychology.

Bemis, K. M. (1985). "Abstinence" and "nonabstinence" models for the treatment of bulimia. *International Journal of Eating Disorders, 4,* 407–437.

Bennett, A. E. (1960). Diagnosis of intermediate stage of alcohol brain disease. *Journal of the American Medical Association, 172,* 1143–1146.

Berg, R., Franzen, M., & Wedding, D. (1987). *Screening for brain impairment: A manual for mental health practice.* New York: Springer.

Beschner, G. (1985). The problem of adolescent drug abuse: An introduction to intervention strategies. In A. S. Friedman & G. M. Beschner (Eds.), *Treatment services for adolescent substance abusers* (DHHS Publication No. ADM 85-1342, pp. 1–12). Washington, DC: U.S. Government Printing Office.

Bettman, O. L. (1974). *The good old days — They were terrible.* New York: Random House.

Billings, A. G., & Moos, R. H. (1983). Psychosocial processes of recovery among alcoholics and their families: Implications for clinicians and program evaluators. *Addictive Behaviors, 8,* 205–218.

Blaszczynski, A. P., Wilson, A. C., McConaghy, N. (1986). Sensation seeking and pathological gambling. *British Journal of Addiction, 81,* 113–117.

Blazer, D. G., & Pennybacker, M. R. (1984). Epidemiology of alcoholism in the elderly. In J. T. Hartford & T. Samorajski (Eds.), *Alcoholism in the elderly* (pp. 25–33). New York: Raven Press.

Bliss, R. E., Garvey, A. J., Heinhold, J. W., & Hitchcock, J. L. (1989). The influence of situation and coping on relapse crisis outcomes after smoking cessation. *Journal of Consulting and Clinical Psychology, 57,* 443–449.

Blume, S. B., & Lesieur, H. R. (1988). Identifying pathological gamblers in your practice: The South Oaks Gambling Screen. *South Oaks Hospital Journal, 1,* 1–6.

Bohman, M., Sigvardsson, S., & Cloninger, C. R. (1981). Maternal inheritance of alcohol abuse: Cross-fostering analysis of adopted women. *Archives of General Psychiatry, 38,* 965–969.

Borg, S., Czarnecka, A., Kvande, H., Mossberg, D., & Sedvall, G. (1983). Clinical conditions and concentrations of MOPEG in cerebrospinal fluid and urine of alcoholic patients during withdrawal. *Science, 213,* 1135–1137.

Bornstein, P. H., & Bornstein, M. T. (1986). *Marital therapy: A behavioral-communications approach.* Elmsford, NY: Pergamon Press.

Bourne, P. G., & Light, E. (1979). Alcohol problems in blacks and women. In J. H. Mendelson & N. K. Mello (Eds.), *The diagnosis and treatment of alcoholism* (pp. 84–123). New York: McGraw-Hill.

Brandon, T. H., Tiffany, S. T., & Baker, T. B. (1986). The process of smoking relapse. In F. M. Tims & C. G. Leukefeld (Eds.), *Relapse and recovery in drug abuse* (DHHS Publication No. ADM 86-1473, pp. 104–117). Washington, DC: U.S. Government Printing Office.

Bratter, T. E., Pennacchia, M. C., & Gauya, D. C. (1985). From methadone maintenance to abstinence: The myth of the metabolic disorder theory. In T. E. Bratter & G. G. Forrest (Eds.), *Alcoholism and substance abuse: Strategies for clinical intervention* (pp. 259–302). New York: Free Press.

Brisman, J., & Siegel, M. (1984). Bulimia and alcoholism: Two sides of the same coin? *Journal of Substance Abuse Treatment, 1,* 113–118.

Bromet, E., & Moos, R. H. (1977). Environmental resources and the posttreatment functioning of alcoholic patients. *Journal of Health and Social Behavior, 18,* 326–338.

Brower, K. J., Blow, F. C., & Beresford, T. P. (1989). Treatment implications of chemical dependency models: An integrative approach. *Journal of Substance Abuse Treatment, 6,* 147–157.

Brown, R. I. F. (1986). Arousal and sensation-seeking components in the general explanation of gambling and gambling addictions. *International Journal of the Addictions, 21,* 1001–1016.

Brown, S. A., Goldman, M. S., Inn, A., & Anderson, L. R. (1980). Expectations of reinforcement from alcohol: Their domain and relation to drinking patterns. *Journal of Consulting and Clinical Psychology, 48,* 419–426.

Brown, S. A. (1985). Reinforcement expectancies and alcoholism treatment outcome after a one-year follow-up. *Journal of Studies on Alcohol, 46,* 304–308.

Brown, S. A., Goldman, M. S., & Christiansen, B. A. (1985). Do alcohol expectancies mediate drinking patterns of adults? *Journal of Consulting and Clinical Psychology, 53,* 512–519.

Brown, S. A., & Schuckit, M. A. (1988). Changes in depression among abstinent alcoholics. *Journal of Studies on Alcohol, 49,* 412–417.

Brown, S. A., Vik, P. W., & Creamer, V. A. (1989). Characteristics of relapse following adolescent substance abuse treatment. *Addictive Behaviors, 14,* 291–300.

Brownell, K. D. (1989, June). When and how to diet. *Psychology Today,* pp. 40–46.

Brownell, K. D., Marlatt, G. A., Lichtenstein, E., & Wilson, G. T. (1986). Understanding and preventing relapse. *American Psychologist, 41,* 765–782.

Brownell, K. D., & Wadden, T. A. (1986). Behavior therapy for obesity: Modern approaches and better results. In K. D. Brownell & J. P. Foreyt (Eds.), *Handbook of eating disorders: Physiology, psychology, and the treatment of obesity, anorexia, and bulimia* (pp. 180–197). New York: Basic Books.

Bulik, C. M. (1987) Drug and alcohol abuse by bulimic women and their families. *Psychiatry, 144,* 1604–1606.

Burling, T. A., Reilly, P. M., Moltzen, J. O., & Ziff, D. C. (1989). Self-efficacy and relapse among inpatient drug and alcohol abusers: A predictor of outcome. *Journal of Studies on Alcohol, 50,* 354–360.

Burns, D. D. (1989). *The feeling good handbook: Using the new mood therapy in everyday life.* New York: William Morrow.

Cacioppo, J. T., & Petty, R. E. (1981). Social psychological procedures for cognitive response assessment: The thought listing technique. In T. V. Merluzzi, C. R. Glass, & M. Genest (Eds.), *Cognitive assessment* (pp. 309–342). New York: Guilford Press.

Cahalan, D., & Room, R. (1974). *Problem drinking among American men.* New Brunswick, NJ: Rutgers Center of Alcohol Studies.

Chaney, E. F. (1989). Social skills training. In R. K. Hester & W. R. Miller (Eds.), *Handbook of alcoholism treatment approaches* (pp. 206–221). Elmsford, NY: Pergamon Press.

Chaney, E. F., Roszell, D. K., & Cummings, C. (1982). Relapse in opiate addicts: A behavioral analysis. *Addictive Behaviors, 7,* 291–297.

Chang, M. M., Kwon, J., Hamada, R. S., & Yahiku, P. (1990). Effect of combined substance use on laboratory markers of alcoholism. *Journal of Studies on Alcohol, 51,* 361–365.

Chiauzzi, E. J. (1990). [Psychosocial relapse factors in a sample of alcoholics and drug addicts]. Unpublished raw data.

Chiauzzi, E. J. (in press). Social skills training for alcoholics: Conceptual, methodological, and treatment issues. In D. G. Gilbert & J. Conley (Eds.), *Personality and social skills: An individual differences approach.* New York: Plenum Press.

Chiauzzi, E. J., & Liljegren, S. (1990). *Staying straight: A relapse prevention workbook for young people.* Holmes Beach, FL: Learning Publications.

Childress, A. R., McLellan, A. T., Ehrman, R., & O'Brien, C. P. (1988). Classically conditioned responses in opioid and cocaine dependence: A role in relapse? In B. A. Ray (Ed.), *Learning factors in substance abuse* (DHHS Publication No. ADM 88-1576, pp. 25–43). Washington, DC: U.S. Government Printing Office.

Christiansen, B. A., Roehling, P. V., Smith, G. T., & Goldman, M. S. (1989). Using alcohol expectancies to predict adolescent drinking behavior after one year. *Journal of Consulting and Clinical Psychology, 57,* 93–99.

Cloninger, C. R., Bohman, M., & Sigvardsson, S. (1981). Inheritance of alcohol abuse. *Archives of General Psychiatry, 38,* 861–868.

Coambs, R. B., Kozlowski, L. T., & Ferrence, R. G. (1989). The future of tobacco use and smoking research. In T. Ney & A. Gale (Eds.), *Smoking and human behavior* (pp. 337–348). New York: John Wiley & Sons.

Cohen, S. (1987). Causes of the cocaine outbreak. In A. M. Washton & M. S. Gold (Eds.), *Cocaine: A clinician's handbook* (pp. 3–9). New York: Guilford Press.

Colletti, G., Supnick, J. A., & Rizzo, A. A. (1982). Long term follow-up (3–4 years) of treatment for smoking reduction. *Addictive Behaviors, 7,* 429–433.

Commission on the Review of National Policy Toward Gambling. (1976). *Gambling in America.* Washington, DC: U.S. Government Printing Office.

Condiotte, M. M., & Lichtenstein, E. (1981). Self-efficacy and relapse in smoking cessation programs. *Journal of Consulting and Clinical Psychology, 49,* 648–658.

Cooper, M. L., Russell, M., & George, W. H. (1988). Coping, expectancies, and alcohol abuse: A test of social learning formulations. *Journal of Abnormal Psychology, 97,* 218–230.

Costello, R. M. (1975a). Alcoholism treatment and evaluation: In search of methods. *International Journal of the Addictions, 10,* 251–275.

Costello, R. M. (1975b). Alcoholism treatment and evaluation: In search of methods. II. Collation of two-year follow-up studies. *International Journal of the Addictions, 10,* 857–867.

Covington, S. (1986). Facing the clinical challenges of women alcoholics: Physical, emotional, and sexual abuse. *Focus on Family, 3,* 10–11.

Cox, W. M. (1986). *The addictive personality.* New York: Chelsea House.

Cronkite, R. C., & Moos, R. H. (1980). Determinants of the posttreatment functioning of alcoholic patients: A conceptual framework. *Journal of Consulting and Clinical Psychology, 48,* 305–316.

Cummings, C., Gordon, J., & Marlatt, G. A. (1980). Relapse: Strategies of prevention and prediction. In W. R. Miller (Ed.), *The addictive behaviors.* (pp. 291–321). Elmsford, NY: Pergamon Press.

Custer, R., & Milt, H. (1985). *When luck runs out: Help for compulsive gamblers and their families.* New York: Warner Books.

Dackis, C., Gold, M. S., & Pottash, A. L. C. (1987). Central stimulant abuse: Neurochemistry and pharmacotherapy. In M. S. Gold & M. Galanter (Eds.), *Cocaine: Pharmacology, addiction, and therapy* (pp. 7–21). New York: Haworth Press.

Daley, D. C. (1986). *Relapse prevention workbook for recovering alcoholics and drug dependent persons.* Holmes Beach, FL: Learning Publications.

Daley, D. C. (1987, March-April). Relapse prevention with substance abusers: Clinical issues and myths. *Social Work, 138*–142.

Derogatis, L. R. (1977). *SCL-90-R: Administration, scoring and procedures manual I.* Baltimore, MD: Johns Hopkins University School of Medicine, Clinical Psychometrics Research Unit.

De Leon, G., & Deitch, D. (1985). Treatment of the adolescent substance abuser in a therapeutic community. In A. S. Friedman & G. M. Beschner (Eds.), *Treatment services for adolescent substance abusers* (DHHS Publication No. ADM 85-1342, pp. 216–230). Washington, DC: U.S. Government Printing Office.

DeSoto, C. B., O'Donnell, W. E., Allred, L. J., & Lopes, C. E. (1985). Symptomatology in alcoholics at various stages of abstinence. *Alcoholism: Clinical and Experimental Research, 9,* 505–512.

Diamant, A. (1989, January 15). "You're trained to care for the sick, the suffering and dying. No one's there to comfort you." *Boston Globe,* pp. 18, 28–40.

DiFranza, J. R., & Guerrera, M. P. (1990). Alcoholism and smoking. *Journal of Studies on Alcohol, 51,* 130–135.

Dole, V. P., & Nyswander, M. E. (1976). Methadone maintenance treatment, a ten-year perspective. *Journal of the American Medical Association, 235,* 2117–2119.

Donovan, D. M. (1988). Assessment of addictive behaviors: Implications of an emerging biopsychosocial model. In D. M. Donovan & G. A. Marlatt (Eds.), *Assessment of addictive behaviors* (pp. 3–48). New York: Guilford Press.

Donovan D. M., & Marlatt, G. A. (1988). *Assessment of addictive behaviors.* New York: Guilford Press.

Drug addicts see smoking as harder habit to kick. (1990, April). *Clinical Psychiatry News,* p. 12.

Dupont, R. L. (1987). Cocaine in the workplace: The ticking time bomb. In A. M. Washton & M. S. Gold (Eds.), *Cocaine: A clinician's handbook* (pp. 192–201). New York: Guilford Press.

D'Zurilla, T. J. (1986). *Problem-solving therapy: A social competence approach to clinical intervention.* New York: Springer.

D'Zurilla, T. J., & Goldfried, M. R. (1971). Problem solving and behavior modification. *Journal of Abnormal Psychology, 78,* 107–126.

Eastman, C., & Norris, H. (1982). Alcohol dependence, relapse, and self-identity. *Journal of Studies on Alcohol, 43,* 1214–1231.

Evaluation consortium data link patient profiles, abstinence rates. (1989, September). *Hazelden Professional Update,* pp. 2–3.

Fagerstrom, K. O. (1978). Measuring degree of physical dependence to tobacco with reference to individualization of treatment. *Addictive Behaviors, 3,* 235–241.

Fairburn, C. B., & Beglin, S. J. (1990). Studies of the epidemiology of bulimia nervosa. *American Journal of Psychiatry, 147,* 401–408.

Filstead, W. J., Parella, D. P., & Ebbitt, J. (1988). High-risk situations for engaging in substance abuse and binge-eating behaviors. *Journal of Studies on Alcohol, 49,* 136–141.

Finney, J. W., Moos, R. H., & Mewborn, C. R. (1980). Posttreatment experiences and treatment outcome of alcoholic patients six months and two years after hospitalization. *Journal of Consulting and Clinical Psychology, 48,* 17–29.

Fiore, M. C., Novotny, T. E., Pierce, J. P., Giovino, G. A., Hatziandreu, E. J., Newcomb, P. A., Surawicz, T. S., & Davis, R. M. (1990). Methods used to quit smoking in the United States: Do cessation programs help? *Journal of the American Medical Association, 263,* 2760–2795.

Fisher, R., & Ury, W. (1981). *Getting to yes: Negotiating agreement without giving in.* New York: Penguin Books.

Folkman, S., & Lazarus, R. (1988). *Ways of coping questionnaire.* Palo Alto, CA: Consulting Psychologists Press.

Freedberg, E. J., & Johnston, W. E. (1980). Outcome with alcoholics seeking treatment voluntarily or after confrontation by their employer. *Journal of Occupational Medicine, 22,* 83–86.

Freeman, S. (1988). *The encyclopedia of psychoactive drugs: Series 2: Drugs and civilization.* New York: Chelsea House.

Friedman, M., & Ulmer, D. (1984). *Treating type A behavior and your heart.* New York: Alfred A. Knopf.

Galizio, M., & Stein, F. S. (1983). Sensation seeking and drug choice. *International Journal of the Addictions, 18,* 1039–1048.

Garner, D. M., & Garfinkel, P. E. (1979). The eating attitudes test: An index of the symptoms of anorexia nervosa. *Psychological Medicine, 9,* 273–279.

Garner, D. M., & Olmsted, M. P. (1984). *The eating disorder inventory manual.* Odessa, FL: Psychological Assessment Resources.

Gawin, F. H., & Kleber, H. D. (1986). Abstinence symptomatology and psychiatric diagnosis in cocaine abusers. *Archives of General Psychiatry, 43,* 107–113.

Gerstley, L. J., Alterman, A. I., McLellan, A. T., & Woody, G. E. (1990). Antisocial personality disorder in patients with substance abuse disorders: A problematic diagnosis? *American Journal of Psychiatry, 147,* 173–178.

Glantz, M. (1981). Predictions of elderly drug abuse. *Journal of Psychoactive Drugs, 13,* 117–126.

Gold, M. S. (1988). *The facts about drugs and alcohol* (3rd ed.). New York: Bantam Books.

Gold, M. S. (1990). *800-COCAINE.* New York: Bantam Books.

Gold, M. S., Washton, A. M., & Dackis, C. A. (1985). Cocaine abuse: Neurochemistry, phenomenology, and treatment. In N. J. Kozel & E. H. Adams (Eds.), *Cocaine use in America: Epidemiologic and clinical perspectives* (DHHS Publication No. ADM 85-1414, pp. 130–150). Washington, DC: U.S. Government Printing Office.

Goldfried, M. R., & Davison, G. C. (1976). *Clinical behavior therapy.* New York: Holt, Rinehart & Winston.

Gomberg, E. L. (1980). *Drinking and problem drinking among the elderly.* Ann Arbor, MI: Institute of Gerontology, University of Michigan.

Goodwin, D. W. (1988). *Is alcoholism hereditary?* (2nd ed.). New York: Ballantine Books.

Goodwin, D. W., Schulsinger, F., Moller, N., Hermansen, L., Winokur, G., & Guze, S. B. (1974). Drinking problems in adopted and nonadopted sons of alcoholics. *Archives of General Psychiatry, 31,* 164–169.

Gormally, J., Rardin, D., & Black, S. (1980). Correlates of successful response to a behavioral weight control clinic. *Journal of Counseling Psychology, 27,* 170–191.

Gorski, T. T. (1986, Fall). Relapse prevention planning: A new recovery tool. *Alcohol Health and Research World,* pp. 6–11, 63.

Gorski, T. T. (1988). *The staying sober workbook: A serious solution for the problem of relapse.* Independence, MO: Independence Press.

Gorski, T. T., & Miller, M. (1986). *Staying sober: A guide for relapse prevention.* Independence, MO: Independence Press.

Gorski, T. T., & Miller, M. (1987). *Mistaken beliefs about relapse.* Independence, MO: Independence Press.

Graham, J. R., & Strenger, V. E. (1988). MMPI characteristics of alcoholics: A review. *Journal of Consulting and Clinical Psychology, 56,* 197–205.

Grant, D. A., & Berg, E. A. (1948). A behavioral analysis of degree of reinforcement and ease of shifting to new responses in a Weigl-type card-sorting problem. *Journal of Experimental Psychology, 38,* 401–411.

Green, B. (1978). The politics of psychoactive drug use in old age. *The Gerontologist, 18,* 525–530.

Griffin, M. L., Weiss, R. D., Mirin, S. M., & Lange, U. (1989). A comparison of male and female cocaine abusers. *Archives of General Psychiatry, 46,* 122–126.

Grilo, C. M., Schiffman, S., & Wing, R. R. (1989). Relapse crises and coping among dieters. *Journal of Consulting and Clinical Psychology, 57,* 488–495.

Haley, J. (1969). *The power tactics of Jesus Christ and other essays.* New York: Avon Books.

Hall, S. M., Havassy, B. E., & Wasserman, D. A. (1990). Commitment to abstinence and acute stress in relapse to alcohol, opiates, and nicotine. *Journal of Consulting and Clinical Psychology, 58,* 175–181.

Hall, S. M., Rugg, D., Tunstall, C., & Jones, R. T. (1984). Preventing relapse to cigarette smoking by behavioral skill training. *Journal of Consulting and Clinical Psychology, 52,* 372–382.

Halstead, W. C. (1947). *Brain and intelligence.* Chicago: University of Chicago Press.

Hammer, A. L., & Marting, M. S. (1987). *Coping resources inventory.* Palo Alto, CA: Consulting Psychologists Press.

Hatsukami, D., Eckert, E., Mitchell, J. E., & Pyle, R. (1984). Affective disorder and substance abuse in women with bulimia. *Psychological Medicine, 24,* 701–704.

Hatsukami, D., Pickens, R. W., & Svikis, D. (1981). Post-treatment depressive symptoms and relapse to drug use in different age groups of an alcohol and other drug abuse population. *Drug and Alcohol Dependence, 8,* 271–277.

Hawkins, J. D., Catalano, R. F., Gillmore, M. R., & Wells, E. A. (1989). Skills training for drug abusers: Generalization, maintenance, and effects on drug use. *Journal of Consulting and Clinical Psychology, 57,* 559–563.

Heather, N., Rollnick, S., & Wilson, M. (1983). A comparison of objective and subjective measures of alcohol dependence as predictors of relapse following treatment. *British Journal of Clinical Psychology, 22,* 11–17.

Hebb, D. (1955). Drives and the C.N.S. *Psychological Review, 62,* 243–253.

Helzer, J. E., Robins, L. N., Taylor, J. R., Carey, K., Miller, R. H., Combs-Orme, T., & Farmer, A. (1985). The extent of long-term moderate drinking among alcoholics discharged from medical and psychiatric treatment facilities. *New England Journal of Medicine, 312,* 1678–1682.

Henningfield, J. E. (1984). Pharmacologic basis and treatment of cigarette smoking. *Journal of Clinical Psychiatry, 45,* 24–34.

Hesselbrock, M. N., Meyer, R. E., & Keener, J. J. (1985). Psychopathology in hospitalized alcoholics. *Archives of General Psychiatry, 42,* 1050–1055.

Hesselbrock, M., Hesselbrock, V., Syzmanski, K., & Weidenman, M. (1988). Suicide attempts and alcoholism. *Journal of Studies on Alcohol, 49,* 436–442.

Hoard, P. S. (1988, July–August). Premenstrual syndrome can trigger relapse. *Alcoholism & Addiction,* pp. 41–42.

Holmes, T. H., & Rahe, R. H. (1967). The social readjustment rating scale. *Journal of Psychosomatic Research, 11,* 213–218.

Horn, J. L., Wanberg, K. W., & Foster, F. M. (1987). *The alcohol use inventory.* Minneapolis, MN: National Computer Systems.

Hrubec, Z., & Omenn, G. S. (1981). Evidence of genetic predisposition to alcohol cirrhosis and psychosis: Twin concordances for alcoholism and its biological end points by zygosity among male veterans. *Alcoholism: Clinical and Experimental Research, 5,* 207–212.

Hubbard, R. L., Cavanaugh, E. R., Craddock, S. G., & Rachal, J. V. (1985). In A. S. Friedman & G. M. Beschner (Eds.), *Treatment services for adolescent substance abusers* (DHHS Publication No. ADM 85-1342, pp. 49–65). Washington, DC: U.S. Government Printing Office.

Hubbard, R. L., Marsden, M. E., Rachal, J. V., Harwood, H. J., Cavanaugh, E. R., & Ginzburg, H. M. (1989). *Drug abuse treatment: A national study of effectiveness.* Chapel Hill, NC: University of North Carolina Press.

Hudson, C. J., & Perkins, S. H. (1984). Panic disorder and alcohol misuse. *Journal of Studies on Alcohol, 45,* 462–464.

Hunt, W. A., Barnett, L. W., & Branch, L. G. (1971). Relapse rates in addiction programs. *Journal of Clinical Psychology, 27,* 455–456.

Hunt, W. A., & Bespalac, D. A. (1974). An evaluation of current methods of modifying smoking behavior. *Journal of Clinical Psychology, 30,* 431–438.

Hurt, R., & Slade, J. (1990, May-June). Nicotine and the treatment center. *Professional Counselor,* pp. 64–73.

Ikard, F. F., Green, D., & Horn, D. (1969). A scale to differentiate between types of smoking as related to management of affect. *International Journal of the Addictions, 4,* 649–659.

Isler, C. (1978). The alcoholic nurse. *Registered Nurse, 41,* 48–55.

Istvan, J., & Matarazzo, J. D. (1984). Tobacco, alcohol, and caffeine use: A review of their interrelationships. *Psychological Bulletin, 95,* 301–326.

Jefferson, L. V., & Ensor, B. E. (1982, April). Help for the helper: Confronting a chemically-impaired colleague. *American Journal of Nursing,* pp. 574–577.

Johnson, C. (1985). Initial consultation for patients with bulimia and anorexia nervosa. In D. M. Garner & P. E. Garfinkel (Eds.), *Handbook of psychotherapy for anorexia nervosa and bulimia* (pp. 19–51). New York: Guilford Press.

Johnson, C. L., Stuckey, M. K., Lewis, L. D., & Schwartz, D. M. (1982). Bulimia: A descriptive study of 316 cases. *International Journal of Eating Disorders, 2,* 3–16.

Johnson, V. E. (1973). *I'll quit tomorrow.* New York: Harper & Row.

Johnston, L. D., O'Malley, P. M., & Bachman, J. G. (1988). *Illicit drug use, smoking, and drinking by America's high school students, college students, and young adults: 1975–1987.* (DHHS Publication No. ADM 89-1602). Washington, DC: U.S. Government Printing Office.

Jonas, J. M., Gold, M. S., Sweeney, D. & Pottash, A. L. C. (1987). Eating disorders and cocaine abuse: A survey of 259 cocaine abusers. *Journal of Clinical Psychiatry. 48,* 47–50.

Kandel, D. B., & Raveis, V. H. (1989). Cessation of drug use in young adulthood. *Archives of General Psychiatry, 46,* 109–116.

Kaplan, R. F., Meyer, R. E., & Stroebel, C. F. (1983). Alcohol dependence and responsivity to an ethanol stimulus as predictors of alcohol consumption. *British Journal of Addiction, 78,* 256–267.

Kaufman, E. (1989). The psychotherapy of dually diagnosed patients. *Journal of Substance Abuse Treatment, 6.* 9–18.

Kennedy, D. (1971). *Pupilometrics as an aid in the assessment of motivation, impact of treatment, and prognosis of chronic alcoholics.* Unpublished doctoral dissertation, University of Utah.

Khantzian, E. J. (1985). The self-medication hypothesis of addictive disorders: Focus on heroin and cocaine dependence. *American Journal of Psychiatry, 142,* 1259–1264.

King, P., & Flaum, J. (1988). *Sex, drugs, and rock and roll.* Bellevue, WA: Professional Counselor Books.

King, A. C., & Frederiksen, L. W. (1984). Low-cost strategies increasing exercise behavior: Relapse preparation training and social support. *Behavior Modification, 8,* 3–21.

Kinney, J. (1983). Relapse among alcoholics who are alcoholism counselors. *Journal of Studies on Alcohol, 44,* 744–748.

Kissin, B. (1979). Biological investigations in alcohol research. *Journal of Studies on Alcohol, 8,* 146–181.

Kivlahan, D. R., Sher, K. J., & Donovan, D. M. (1989). The alcohol dependence scale: A validation study among inpatient alcoholics. *Journal of Studies on Alcohol, 50,* 170–175.

Kleber, H. D., & Gawin, F. H. (1987). Pharmacological treatments of cocaine abuse. In A. M. Washton & M. S. Gold (Eds.), *Cocaine: A clinician's handbook* (pp. 118–134). New York: Guilford Press.

Kosten, T. A., Kosten, T. R., & Rounsaville, B. J. (1989). Personality disorders in opiate addicts show prognostic specificity. *Journal of Substance Abuse Treatment, 6,* 163–168.

Kosten, T. R., Jalali, B., Steidl, J. H., & Kleber, H. D. (1987). Relationship of marital structure and interactions to opiate abuse relapse. *American Journal of Drug and Alcohol Abuse, 13,* 387–399.

Kosten, T. R., & Kleber, H. D. (1988). Differential diagnosis of psychiatric comorbidity in substance abusers. *Journal of Substance Abuse Treatment, 5,* 201–206.

Knapp, T. J., & Lech, B. C. (1987). Pathological gambling: A review with recommendations. *Advances in Behaviour Research and Therapy, 9,* 21–49.

Krippenstapel, P. (1988). Genetic alcoholism and risk of relapse. In D. Daley (Ed.), *Relapse: Conceptual, research, and clinical perspectives* (pp. 53–66). New York: Haworth Press.

Kushner, M. G., Sher, K. J., & Beitman, B. D. (1990). The relation between alcohol problems and the anxiety disorders. *American Journal of Psychiatry, 147,* 685–695.

Laliotis, D. A., & Grayson, J. H. (1985). Psychologist heal thyself: What is available for the impaired psychologist. *American Psychologist, 40,* 84–96.

Leber, W. R., Parsons, O. A., & Nichols, N. (1985). Neuropsychological test results are related to ratings of men alcoholics' therapeutic progress: A replicated study. *Journal of Studies on Alcohol, 46,* 116–121.

Leigh, B. C. (1987). Beliefs about the effects of alcohol on self and others. *Journal of Studies on Alcohol, 48,* 467–475.

Leigh, B. C. (1989a). In search of the seven dwarves: Issues of measurement and meaning in alcohol expectancy research. *Psychological Bulletin, 105,* 361–373.

Leigh, B. C. (1989b). Attitudes and expectancies as predictors of drinking habits: A comparison of three scales. *Journal of Studies on Alcohol, 50,* 432–440.

Leon, G., & Chamberlain, K. (1973). Emotional arousal, eating patterns and body image as differential factors associated with varying success in maintaining a weight loss. *Journal of Consulting and Clinical Psychology, 40,* 474–480.

Lesieur, H. R. (1986). *Understanding compulsive gambling.* Center City, MN: Hazelden Educational Materials.

Lesieur, H. R., Blume, S. B. & Zoppa, R. M. (1986). Alcoholism, drug abuse, and gambling. *Alcoholism: Clinical and experimental research, 10,* 33–38.

Lew, M. (1988). *Victims no more: Men recovering from incest and other sexual child abuse.* New York: Harper & Row.

Lex, B. W. (1985). Alcohol problems in special populations. In J. H. Mendelson & N. J. Mello (Eds.), *The diagnosis and treatment of alcoholism* (pp. 89–117). New York: McGraw-Hill.

Lindesmith, A. R. (1968). *Addiction and Opiates.* Chicago: Aldine.

Litman, G. K., Eiser, J. R., Rawson, N. S. B., & Oppenheim, A. N. (1977). Towards a typology of relapse: A preliminary report. *Drug and Alcohol Dependence, 2,* 157–162.

Litman, G. K., Eiser, J. R., & Taylor, C. (1979). Dependence, relapse and extinction: A theoretical critique and a behavioral explanation. *Journal of Clinical Psychology, 35,* 192–199.

Litman, G. K., Stapleton, J., Oppenheim, A. N. & Peleg, M. (1983). An instrument for measuring coping behaviours in hospitalized alcoholics. *British Jounal of Addiction, 78,* 269–276.

Litman, G. K., Stapleton, J., Oppenheim, A. N., Peleg, M., & Jackson, P. (1983). Situations related to alcoholism relapse. *British Journal of Addiction, 78,* 381–389.

Ludwig, A. M. (1988). *Understanding the alcoholic's mind: The nature of craving and how to control it.* New York: Oxford University Press.

Ludwig, A. M., & Wikler, A. (1974). The first drink: Psychobiological aspects of craving. *Archives of General Psychiatry, 30,* 539–547.

MacAndrew, C. (1965). The differentiation of male alcoholic outpatients by means of the MMPI. *Quarterly Journal of Studies on Alcohol, 26,* 238–246.

Maddux, J. F., & Desmond, D. P. (1986). Relapse and recovery in substance abuse careers. In F. M. Tims & C. G. Leukefeld (Eds.), *Relapse and recovery in drug abuse* (DHHS Publication No. ADM 86-1473, pp. 49–71). Washington, DC: U.S. Government Printing Office.

Maddux, J. F., Desmond, D. P., & Esquivel, M. (1980). Outpatient methadone withdrawal for heroin dependence. *American Journal of Drug and Alcohol Abuse, 7,* 323–333.

Marks, S. J., Daroff, L. J. & Granick, S. (1985). In A. S. Friedman & G. M. Beschner (Eds.), *Treatment services for adolescent substance abusers* (DHHS Publication No. ADM 85-1342, pp. 94–111). Washington, DC: U.S. Government Printing Office.

Marlatt, G. A. (1985a). Cognitive factors in the relapse process. In G. A. Marlatt & J. R. Gordon (Eds.), *Relapse prevention: Maintenance strategies in the treatment of addictive behavior* (pp. 128–200). New York: Guilford Press.

Marlatt, G. A. (1985b). Relapse prevention: Theoretical rationale and overview of the model. In G. A. Marlatt & J. R. Gordon (Eds.), *Relapse prevention: Maintenance strategies in the treatment of addictive behaviors* (pp. 3–70). New York: Guilford Press.

Marlatt, G. A. (1985c). Cognitive assessment and intervention procedures for relapse prevention. In G. A. Marlatt & J. R. Gordon (Eds.), *Relapse prevention: Maintenance strategies in the treatment of addictive behavior* (pp. 201–279). New York: Guilford Press.

Marlatt, G. A. (1985d). Lifestyle modification. In G. A. Marlatt & J. R. Gordon (Eds.), *Relapse prevention: Maintenance strategies in the treatment of addictive behavior* (pp. 280–348). New York: Guilford Press.

Marlatt, G. A., Demming, B., & Reid, J. B. (1973). Loss of control drinking in alcoholics: An experimental analogue. *Journal of Abnormal Psychology, 81,* 223–241.

Marlatt, G. A., & Gordon, J. R. (1980). Determinants of relapse: Implications for the maintenance of behavior change. In P. O. Davidson & S. M. Davidson (Eds.), *Behavioral medicine: Changing health lifestyles* (pp. 410–452). Elmsford, NY: Pergamon Press.

Marlatt, G. A., & Gordon, J. R. (Eds.). (1985). *Relapse prevention.* New York: Guilford Press.

Marlatt, G. A. & Miller, W. R. (1984). *Comprehensive drinker profile.* Odessa, FL: Psychological Assessment Resources.

Marlatt, G. A., & Rohsenow, D. J. (1980). Cognitive process in alcohol use: Expectancy and the balanced placebo design. In N. K. Mello (Ed.), *Advances in substance abuse* (Vol. 1, pp. 159–199). Greenwich, CT: JAI Press.

Martin, J. E., & Dubbert, P. M. (1986). Exercise and health: The adherence problem. *Behavioral Medicine Update, 4,* 16–24.

McAuliffe, W. E., & Ch'ien, J. M. N. (1986). Recovery training and self-help: A relapse-prevention program for treated opiate addicts. *Journal of Substance Abuse Treatment, 3,* 9–20.

McAuliffe, W. E., Feldman, B., Friedman, R., Launer, E., Magnuson, E., Mahoney, C., Santangelo, S., & Ward, W. (1986). Explaining relapse to opiate addiction following successful completion of treatment. In F. M. Tims & C. G. Leukefeld (Eds.), *Relapse and recovery in drug abuse* (DHHS Publication No. ADM 86-1473, pp. 136–156). Washington, DC: U.S. Government Printing Office.

McBride, C. M., & Pirie, P. L. (1990). Postpartum smoking relapse. *Addictive Behaviors, 15,* 165–168.

McCance, C., & McCance, P. F. (1969). Alcoholism in north-east Scotland: Its treatment and outcome. *British Journal of Psychiatry, 115,* 189–198.

McCarthy, W. J. (1985). The cognitive developmental model and other alternatives to the social skills deficit model of smoking onset. In C. S. Bell & R. Battjes (Eds.), *Prevention research: Deterring drug abuse among children and adolescents* (DHHS Publication No. ADM 87-1334, pp. 153–169). Washington, DC: U.S. Government Printing Office.

McCrady, B. S. (1987). Implications of neuropsychological research findings for the treatment and rehabilitation of alcoholics. In O. A. Parsons, N. Butters, & P. E. Nathan, (Eds.), *Neuropsychology of alcoholism: Implications for diagnosis and treatment* (pp. 381–391). New York: Guilford Press.

McCrady, B. S. (1989). Extending relapse prevention models to couples. *Addictive Behaviors, 14,* 69–74.

McCrady, B. S., & Sher, K. J. (1983). Alcoholism treatment approaches: Patient variables, treatment variables. In B. Tabakoff, P. B. Sutker, & C. L. Randall (Eds.), *Medical and social aspects of alcohol abuse* (pp. 309–373). New York: Plenum Press.

McCrady, B. S., & Smith D. E. (1986). Implications of cognitive impairment for the treatment of alcoholism. *Alcoholism: Clinical and experimental research, 10,* 145–149.

McLellan, A. T., Luborsky, L., Woody, G. E., & O'Brien, C. P. (1980). An improved diagnostic evaluation instrument for substance abuse patients: The addiction severity index. *The Journal of Nervous and Mental Disease, 168,* 26–33.

McLellan, A. T., Luborsky, L., Woody, G. E., O'Brien, C. P., & Druley, K. A. (1983). Predicting response to alcohol and drug abuse treatments: The role of psychiatric severity. *Archives of General Psychiatry, 40,* 620–625.

McLellan, A. T., O'Brien, C. P., Kron, R., Alterman, A. L., & Druley, K. A. (1980). Matching substance abuse patients to appropriate treatments: A conceptual and methodological approach. *Drug and Alcohol Dependence, 5,* 189–195.

Mello, N. K. (1986). Drug use patterns and premenstrual dysphoria. In B. A. Ray & M. C. Brande (Eds.), *Women and drugs: A new era for research* (DHHS Publication No. ADM 87-1447, pp. 31–48). Washington, DC: U.S. Government Printing Office.

Meichenbaum, D., & Turk, D. C. (1987). *Facilitating treatment adherence: A practitioner's guidebook.* New York: Plenum Press.

Milam, J. R., & Ketcham, K. (1981). *Under the influence: A guide to the myths and realities of alcoholism.* New York: Bantam Books.

Milkman, H., & Sunderwirth, S. (1987). *Craving for ecstasy: The consciousness and chemistry of escape.* Lexington, MA: Lexington Books.

Miller, W. R. (1985). Motivation for treatment: A review with special emphasis on alcoholism. *Psychological Bulletin, 98,* 84–107.

Miller, W. R. (1989). Increasing motivation for change. In R. K. Hester & W. R. Miller (Eds.), *Handbook of alcoholism treatment approaches* (pp. 67–80). Elmsford, NY: Pergamon Press.

Miller, W. R., & Hester, R. K. (1980). Treating the problem drinker: Modern approaches. In W. R. Miller (Ed.), *The addictive behaviors: Treatment of alcoholism, drug abuse, smoking, and obesity* (pp. 11–141). Elmsford, NY: Pergamon Press.

Miller, W. R., & Hester, R. K. (1986). The effectiveness of alcoholism treatment: What the research reveals. In W. R. Miller & N. Heather (Eds.), *Treating addictive behaviors: Processes of change* (pp. 121–174). New York: Plenum Press.

Miller, W. R., & Hester, R. K. (1987, November). *Problem drinking: Assessment, motivation, and intervention.* Pre-convention institute presented at the annual meeting of the Association for the Advancement of Behavior Therapy, Philadelphia, PA.

Miller, W. R., & Saucedo, C. F. (1983). Assessment of neuropsychological impairment and brain damage in problem drinkers. In C. J. Golden, J. A. Moses, J. A. Coffman, W. R. Miller, & F. D. Strider (Eds.), *Clinical neuropsychology: Interface with neurologic and psychiatric disorders* (pp. 141–195). New York: Grune & Stratton.

Miller, P. M., Smith, G. T., & Goldman, M. S. (1990). Emergence of alcohol expectancies in childhood: A possible critical period. *Journal of Studies on Alcohol, 51,* 343–349.

Mirin, S. M., Weiss, R. D., Michael, J., & Griffin, M. L. (1988). Psychopathology in substance abusers: Diagnosis and treatment. *American Journal of Drug and Alcohol Abuse, 14,* 139–157.

Mitchell, J. E., Hoberman, J., & Pyle, R. L. (1989). An overview of the treatment of bulimia nervosa. *Psychiatric Medicine, 7,* 317–332.

Monti, P. M., Abrams, D. B., Binkoff, J. A., & Zwick, W. R. (1986). Social skills training and substance abuse. In C. R. Hollin & P. Trower (Eds.), *Handbook of social skills training* (Vol. 2, pp. 111–142). Elmsford, NY: Pergamon Press.

Monti, P. M., Abrams, D. B., Kadden, R. M., & Cooney, N. L. (1989). *Treating alcohol dependence.* New York: Guilford Press.

Monti, P. M., Binkoff, J. A., Zwick, W. R., Abrams, D. B., Nirenberg, T. D., & Liepman, M. R. (1987). Reactivity of alcoholics and nonalcoholics to drinking cues. *Journal of Abnormal Psychology, 96,* 122–126.

Moos, R. H. (1986). *Work environment scale manual, (2nd ed.)*. Palo Alto, CA: Consulting Psychologists Press.

Moos, R. H., & Bliss, R. (1978). Difficulty of follow-up and alcoholism treatment outcome. *Journal of Studies on Alcohol, 39,* 473–490.

Moos, R. H., Finney, J. W., & Chan, D. A. (1981). The process of recovery from alcoholism: I. Comparing alcoholic patients and matched community controls. *Journal of Studies on Alcohol, 42,* 383–402.

Moos, R. H., Finney, J. W., & Cronkite, R. C. (1990). *Alcoholism treatment: Context, process, and outcome.* New York: Oxford University Press.

Moos, R., & Moos, B. (1986). *Family environment scale manual: Second edition.* Palo Alto, CA: Consulting Psychologists Press.

Mossberg, D., Liljeberg, P., & Borg, S. (1985). Clinical conditions in alcoholics during long-term abstinence: A descriptive, longitudinal treatment study. *Alcohol, 2,* 551–553.

Musto, D. F. (1987). *The American disease: Origins of narcotic control.* New York: Oxford University Press.

Myers, M. G., & Brown, S. A. (1990). Coping responses and relapse among adolescent substance abusers. *Journal of Substance Abuse, 2,* 177–189.

Nathan, P. E., & Skinstad, A. (1987). Outcomes of treatment for alcohol problems: Current methods, problems, and results. *Journal of Consulting and Clinical Psychology, 55,* 332–340.

Newcomb, M. D. & Bentler, P. M. (1986). Cocaine use among adolescents: Longitudinal associations with social context, psychopathology, and use of other substances. *Addictive Behaviors, 11,* 263–273.

Niaura, R. S., Rohsenow, D. J., Binkoff, J. A., Monti, P. M., Pedraza, M., & Abrams, D. B. (1988). Relevance of cue reactivity to understanding alcohol and smoking relapse. *Journal of Abnormal Psychology, 97,* 133–152.

Nowack, C. (1985). Life events and drinking behavior in later years. In E. Gottheil, K. A. Druley, T. E. Skoloda, & H. M. Waxman (Eds.), *The combined problems of alcoholism, drug addiction, and aging* (pp. 36–49). Springfield, IL: Charles C Thomas.

O'Farrell, T. J. (1990). Marital and family therapy: Implications of research for alcoholism treatment. In P. Block (Chair), *Recent advances in addictions treatment.* Symposium conducted at the 98th Annual Convention of the American Psychological Association at Boston, August, 1990.

O'Farrell, T. J., & Cowles, K. S. (1989). Marital and family therapy. In R. K. Hester & W. R. Miller (Eds.), *Handbook of alcoholism treatment approaches* (pp. 183–205). Elmsford, NY: Pergamon Press.

O'Leary, M. R., Donovan, D. M., Chaney, E. F., & Walker, R. D. (1979). Cognitive impairment and treatment outcome with alcoholics: Preliminary findings. *Journal of Clinical Psychiatry, 40,* 397–398.

Orford, J., & Hawker, A. (1974). An investigation of an alcoholism rehabilitation halfway house: II. The complex question of client motivation. *British Journal of Addiction, 69,* 315–323.

Ornstein, P., & Cherepon, A. (1985). Demographic variables as predictors of alcoholism treatment outcome. *Journal of Studies on Alcohol, 46,* 425–432.

Parsons, O. A. (1987). Neuropsychological aspects of alcohol abuse: Many questions—some answers. In O. A. Parsons, M. Butters, & P. Nathan (Eds.), *Neuropsychology of alcoholism: Implications for diagnosis and treatment* (pp. 392–403). New York: Guilford Press.

Peele, S. (Ed.). (1985). *The meaning of addiction: A compulsive experience and its interpretation.* Lexington, MA: Lexington Books.

Peele, S. (1990). *Diseasing of America: Addiction treatment out of control.* Lexington, MA: Lexington Books.

Penick, E. C., Powell, B. J., Liskow, B. I., Jackson, J. O., & Nickel, E. J. (1988). The stability of coexisting psychiatric syndromes in alcoholic men after one year. *Journal of Studies on Alcohol, 49,* 395–405.

Perkins, K. A. (1988). Maintaining smoking abstinence after myocardial infarction. *Journal of Substance Abuse, 1,* 91–107.

Pettinati, H. M., Sugerman, A. A., & Maurer, H. S. (1982). Four year MMPI changes in abstinent and drinking alcoholics. *Alcoholism: Clinical and Experimental Research, 6,* 487–494.

Phillips, J., & Wynne, R. D. (1980). *Cocaine: The mystique and the reality.* New York: Avon Books.

Pickens, R. W., & Svikis, D. S. (1988). Genetic vulnerability to drug abuse. In R. W. Pickens & D. S. Svikis (Eds.), *Biological vulnerability to drug abuse* (DHHS Publication No. ADM 88-1590, pp. 1–7). Washington, DC: U.S. Government Printing Office.

Pierce, J. P. Fiore, M. C., Novotny, T. E., Hatziandreu, E. J., Davis, R. M. (1989). Trends in cigarette smoking in the United States: Projections to the year 2000. *Journal of the American Medical Association, 261,* 61–65.

Poikolanien, K., & Saila, S. L. (1986). Drunkenness arrests: Predictors of recurrence and effect of detoxification treatment. *Journal of Studies on Alcohol, 47,* 409–412.

Polich, J. M., Armor, D. J., & Braiker, H. B. (1981). *The course of alcoholism: Four years after treatment.* New York: John Wiley & Sons.

Porjesz, B., & Begleiter, H. (1983). Brain dysfunction and alcohol. In B. Kissin & H. Begleiter (Eds.), *The biology of alcoholism, Vol. 7. The pathogenesis of alcoholism: Biological factors,* (pp. 415–483). New York: Plenum Press.

Prochaska, J. O., & DiClemente, C. C. (1986). Toward a comprehensive model of change. In W. R. Miller & N. Heather (Eds.), *Treating addictive behaviors* (pp. 3–27). New York: Plenum Press.

Prugh, T. (1986, Fall). Recovery without treatment. *Alcohol Health and Research World,* pp. 24–25.

Pursch, J. A. (1985). *Dear Doc.* Minneapolis, MN: CompCare.

Ramirez, L. F., McCormick, R. A., Russo, A. M. & Taber, J. I. (1984). Patterns of substance abuse in pathological gamblers undergoing treatment. *Addictive Behaviors, 8,* 425–428.

Rees, D. W. (1985). Health beliefs and compliance with alcoholism treatment. *Journal of Studies on Alcohol, 46,* 517–524.

Rimmele, C. T., Miller, W. R. & Dougher, M. J. (1989). Aversion therapies. In R. K. Hester & W. R. Miller (Eds.), *Handbook of alcoholism treatment approaches.* Elmsford, NY: Pergamon Press.

Rohsenow, D. J., Corbett, R., & Devine, D. (1988). Molested as children: A hidden contribution to substance abuse? *Journal of Substance Abuse Treatment, 5,* 13–18.

Rohsenow, D. J., Monti, P. M., Zwick, W. R., Nirenberg, T. D., Liepman, M. R., Binkoff, J. A., & Abrams, D. A. (1989). Irrational beliefs, urges to drink and drinking among alcoholics. *Journal of Studies on Alcohol, 50,* 461–464.

Rosenberg, H. (1983). Relapsed versus non-relapsed alcohol abusers: Coping skills, life events, and social support. *Addictive Behaviors, 8,* 183–186.

Rosenberg, C. M., & Liftik, J. (1976). Use of coercion in the outpatient treatment of alcoholism. *Journal of Studies on Alcohol, 37,* 58–65.

Rosenthal, B. S., & Marx, R. D. (1981). Determinants of initial relapse episodes among dieters. *Obesity and Bariatric Medicine, 10,* 94–97.

Rosin, A. J., & Glatt, M. M. (1971). Alcohol excess in the elderly. *Quarterly Journal of Studies on Alcohol, 32,* 53–59.

Ross, H. E., Glaser, F. B., & Germanson, T. (1988). The prevalence of psychiatric disorders in patients with alcohol and other drug problems. *Archives of General Psychiatry, 45,* 1023–1031.

Rounsaville, B. J., Dolinsky, Z. S., Babor, T. F., & Meyer, R. E. (1987). Psychopathology as a predictor of treatment outcome in alcoholics, *Archives General Psychiatry, 44,* 505–513.

Rounsaville, B. J., Weissman, M. M., Kleber, H., & Wilber, C. (1982). Heterogeneity of psychiatric diagnosis in treated opiate addicts. *Archives of General Psychiatry, 39,* 161–166.

Roy, A., Adinoff, B., Roehrich, L., Lamparski, D., Custer, R., Lorenz, V., Barbaccia, M.,

Guidotti, A., Costa, E., & Linnoila, M. (1988). Pathological gambling: A psychobiological study. *Archives of General Psychiatry, 45,* 369–373.

Russo, A. M., Taber, J. J., McCormick, R. A, and Ramirez, L. F. (1984). An outcome study of an inpatient treatment program for pathological gamblers. *Hospital Community Psychiatry, 35,* 823–827.

Rustin, T. A. (1989). *Quit and stay quit.* Houston, TX: Discovery Publishing Company.

Sandahl, C. (1984). Determinants of relapse among alcoholics: A cross-cultural replication study. *International Journal of the Addictions, 19,* 833–848.

Schachter, S. (1982). Recidivism and self-cure of smoking and obesity. *American Psychologist, 37,* 436–444.

Schiffman, S. (1982). Relapse following smoking cessation: A situational analysis. *Journal of Consulting and Clinical Psychology, 50,* 71–86.

Schiffman, S. (1984). Coping with temptations to smoke. *Journal of Consulting and Clinical Psychology, 52,* 261–267.

Schiffman, S. (1988). Behavioral assessment. In D. M. Donovan & G. A. Marlatt (Eds.), *Assessment of addictive behaviors* (pp. 139–188). New York: Guilford Press.

Schiffman, S., & Jarvik, M. E. (1976). Trends in withdrawal symptoms in abstinence from cigarette smoking. *Psychopharmacologia, 50,* 35–39.

Schiffman, S., Read, L., Maltese, J., Rapkin, D., & Jarvik, M. E. (1985). Preventing relapse in ex-smokers: A self-management approach. In G. A. Marlatt & J. R. Gordon (Eds.), *Relapse prevention: Maintenance strategies in the treatment of addictive behaviors* (pp. 472–520). New York: Guilford Press.

Schneier, F. R., & Siris, S. G. (1987). A review of psychoactive substance use and abuse in schizophrenia patterns of drug choice. *Journal of Nervous and Mental Disease, 175,* 641–652.

Schuckit, M. A. (1978). Alcoholism in women. *Advances in Alcoholism, 1,* 1–3.

Schuckit, M. A. (1984). Subjective responses to alcohol in sons of alcoholics and controls. *Archives of General Psychiatry, 41,* 879–884.

Schuckit, M. A. (1985). The clinical implications of primary diagnostic groups among alcoholics. *Archives of General Psychiatry, 42,* 1043–1049.

Schuckit, M. A. (1987). Biological vulnerability to alcoholism. *Journal of Consulting and Clinical Psychology, 55,* 301–309.

Schuckit, M. A., Goodwin, D. W., & Winokur, G. (1972). A half-sibling study of alcoholism. *American Journal of Psychiatry, 128,* 1132–1136.

Schuckit, M. A., & Miller, P. L. (1976). Alcoholism in elderly men: A survey of a general medical ward. *Annals of the New York Academy of Sciences, 273,* 558–571.

Schwarz, R. M., Burkhart, B. R., & Green, S. B. (1978). Turning on or turning off: Sensation seeking or tension reduction as motivational determinants of alcohol use. *Journal of Consulting and Clinical Psychology, 46,* 1144–1145.

Searles, J. S. (1988). The role of genetics in the pathogenesis of alcoholism. *Journal of Abnormal Psychology, 97,* 153–167.

Selzer, M. L. (1971). The Michigan alcohol screening test: The quest for a new diagnostic instrument. *American Journal of Psychiatry, 127,* 1653–1658.

Shaffer, H. J., & Jones, S. B. (1989). *Quitting cocaine: The struggle against impulse.* Lexington, MA: Lexington Books.

Shapiro, D. (1965). *Neurotic styles.* New York: Basic Books.

Shedler, J., & Block J. (1990). Adolescent drug use and psychological health. *American Psychologist, 45,* 612–630.

Shipley, W. C. (1967). *Manual: Shipley-Institute of Living scale.* Los Angeles: Western Psychological Services.

Shisslak, C. M., Schnaps, L. S., & Crago, M. (1989). Eating disorders and substance abuse in women: A comparative study of MMPI patterns. *Journal of Substance Abuse, 1,* 209–219.

Siegal, M., Brisman, J., & Weinshel, M. (1988). *Surviving an eating disorder.* New York: Harper & Row.

Siegel, R. K. (1987). Cocaine smoking: Nature and extent of coca paste and cocaine free-base abuse. In A. M. Washton & M. S. Gold (Eds.), *Cocaine: A clinician's handbook* (pp. 175–191). New York: Guilford Press.

Skinner, H. A. (1982). The drug abuse screening test. *Addictive Behaviors, 7,* 363–371.

Skinner, H., & Allen, B. A. (1982). Alcohol dependence syndrome: Measurement and validation. *Journal of Abnormal Psychology, 91,* 199–209.

Skinner, H. A., & Horn, J. W. (1984). *Alcohol dependence scale: A user's guide.* Toronto, Canada: Addiction Research Foundation.

Smart, R. G. (1976). Spontaneous recovery in alcoholics: A review and analysis of available research. *Drug and Alcohol Dependence, 1,* 277–285.

Smokers's problems go well beyond smoking. (1988, August 23). *Wall Street Journal,* p. 2.

Solomon, J. (1989). Alcoholism and psychiatric disorders. In H. W. Goedde & D. P. Agarwal (Eds.), *Alcoholism: Biomedical and genetic aspects.* Elmsford, NY: Pergamon Press.

Southwick, L., Steele, C., Marlatt, G. A., & Lindell, M. (1981). Alcohol-related expectancies: Defined by phase of intoxication and drinking experience. *Journal of Consulting and Clinical Psychology, 49,* 713–721.

Spendermenders. (1986). San Francisco, CA: Author.

Spitzer, R. L., Williams, J. B. W., Gibbon, M., & First, M. B. (1990). *Structured clinical interview for DSM-III-R: Patient edition (SCID-P, Version 1.0).* Washington, DC: American Psychiatric Press.

Steele, C. M., & Josephs, R. A. (1988). Drinking your troubles away II: An attention-allocation model of alcohol's effect on psychological stress. *Journal of Abnormal Psychology, 97,* 196–205.

Steele, C. M., Southwick, L., & Pagano, R. (1986). Drinking your troubles away: The role of activity in mediating alcohol's reduction of psychological stress. *Journal of Abnormal Psychology, 95,* 173–180.

Stephens, R., & Cottrell, E. (1972). A followup study of 200 narcotic addicts committed for treatment under the Narcotic Rehabilitation Act (NARA). *British Journal of Addiction, 67,* 45–53.

Sternberg, B. (1985). Relapse in weight control: Definitions, processes, and prevention strategies. In G. A. Marlatt & J. R. Gordon (Eds.), *Relapse prevention: Maintenance strategies in the treatment of addictive behaviors* (pp. 521–545). New York: Guilford Press.

Stevens, V. J., & Hollis, J. F. (1989). Preventing smoking relapse, using an individually tailored skill-training technique. *Journal of Consulting and Clinical Psychology, 57,* 420–424.

Stimmel, B., & Rabin, J. (1974). The ability to remain abstinent upon leaving methadone maintenance: A prospective study. *American Journal of Drug and Alcohol Abuse, 1,* 379–391.

Striegel-Moore, R. H., Silberstein, L. R., & Rodin, J. (1986). Toward an understanding of risk factors for bulimia. *American Psychologist, 41,* 246–263.

Stunkard, A. J. (1958). The management of obesity. *New York State Journal of Medicine, 58,* 79–87.

Sulloway, F. J. (1979). *Freud: Biologist of the mind.* New York: Basic Books.

Sutker, P. B., & Allain, A. N. (1988). Issues in personality conceptualizations of addictive behaviors. *Journal of Consulting and Clinical Psychology, 56,* 172–182.

Swaim, R. C., Oetting, E. R., Edwards, R. W., & Beauvais, F. (1989). Links from emotional distress to adolescent drug use: A path model. *Journal of Consulting and Clinical Psychology, 57,* 227–231.

Talbott, G. D., & Martin, C. A. (1984). Relapse and recovery: Special issues for chemically dependent physicians. *Journal of the Medical Association of Georgia, 73,* 763–769.

Tamerin, J. (1985). The psychotherapy of alcoholic women. In S. Zimberg, J. Wallace, & S. B. Blume (Eds.), *Practical approaches to alcoholism psychotherapy* (2nd ed., pp. 259–279). New York: Plenum Press.

Tarter, R. E. (1988). Are there inherited behavioral traits that predispose to substance abuse? *Journal of Consulting and Clinical Psychology, 56,* 189–196.

Tarter, R. E., & Alterman, A. I. (1984). Neuropsychological deficits in alcoholics: Etiological considerations. *Journal of Studies in Alcohol, 45,* 1–9.

Tarter, R. E., Hegedus, A. M., & Gavaler, J. S. (1985). Hyperactivity in sons of alcoholics. *Journal of Studies on Alcohol, 46,* 259–261.

Tennant, F. (1988, Spring–Summer). Clinical diagnosis and treatment of post drug impairment syndrome. *Fair Oaks Hospital Psychiatry Letter,* 47–51.

Thoresen, R. W., Nathan, P. E., Skorina, J. K., & Kilburg, R. R. (1983). The alcoholic psychologist: Issues, problems, and implications for the profession. *Professional Psychology: Research and Practice, 14,* 670–684.

Trachtenberg, M. C., & Blum, K. (1987). Alcohol and opioid peptides: Neuropharmacological rationale for physical craving of alcohol. *American Journal of Drug and Alcohol Abuse, 13,* 365–372.

U.S. Public Health Service. (1989). *The health consequences of smoking: Nicotine addiction: A report of the Surgeon General* (DHHS Publication No. CDC 88-8406). Rockville, MD: Department of Health and Human Services.

Vaillant, G. E. (1983). *The natural history of alcoholism: Causes, patterns, and paths to recovery.* Cambridge, MA: Harvard University Press.

Walker, R. D., Donovan, D. M., Kirlahan, D. R., & O'Leary, M. R. (1983). Length of stay, neuropsychological performance, and aftercare: Influences on Alcohol Treatment outcome. *Journal of Consulting and Clinical Psychology, 51,* 900–911.

Wallace, B. C. (1989). Psychological and environmental determinants of relapse in crack cocaine smokers. *Journal of Substance Abuse Treatment, 6,* 95–106.

Wallace, J. (1988). The relevance to clinical care of recent research in neurobiology. *Journal of Substance Abuse Treatment, 5,* 207–217.

Wallace, J. (1989). *On the new disease model of alcoholism.* Newport, RI: Edgehill Publications.

Wallace, J., McNeill, D., Gilfillan, D., MacLean, K., & Fanella, F. (1988). I. Six-month treatment outcomes in socially stable alcoholics: Abstinence rates. *Journal of Substance Abuse Treatment, 5,* 247–252.

Washton, A. M. (1987). Structured outpatient treatment of cocaine abuse. In M. S. Gold & M. Galanter (Eds.), *Cocaine: Pharmacology, addiction, and therapy* (pp. 143–157). New York: Haworth Press.

Washton, A. M. (1989). *Cocaine addiction: Treatment, recovery, and relapse prevention.* New York: W W Norton.

Washton, A. M., & Gold, M. S. (1987). Recent trends in cocaine abuse as seen from the "800-Cocaine" hotline. In A. M. Washton, & M. S. Gold (Eds.), *Cocaine: A Clinician's Handbook* (pp. 10–22). New York: Guilford Press.

Washton, A. M., Stone, N. S., & Hendrickson, E. C. (1988). Cocaine abuse. In D. M. Donovan & G. A. Marlatt (Eds.), *Assessment of addictive behaviors* (pp. 364–389). New York: Guilford Press.

Washton, A. M., & Stone-Washton, N. (1990). Abstinence and relapse in outpatient cocaine addicts. *Journal of Psychoactive Drugs, 22,* 135–147.

Wechsler, D. A. (1945). A standardized memory scale for clinical use. *Journal of Psychology, 19,* 87–95.

Wechsler, D. A. (1981). *Manual for the Wechsler adult intelligence scale-revised.* New York: Psychological Corporation.

Weiss, L., Katzman, M., & Wolchik, S. (1985). *Treating bulimia: A psychoeducational approach.* Elmsford, NY: Pergamon Press.

Wellman, M. (1954). The late withdrawal symptoms of alcoholic addiction. *Canadian Medical Association Journal, 70,* 526–529.

Wesson, D. R., Havassy, B. E., & Smith, D. E. (1986). Theories of relapse and recovery and their implications for drug abuse treatment. In F. M. Tims & C. G. Leukefeld (Eds.), *Relapse and recovery in drug abuse* (DHHS Publication No. ADM 86-1473, pp. 5–19). Washington, DC: U.S. Government Printing Office.

Westermeyer, J. (1989). Nontreatment factors affecting treatment outcome in substance abuse. *American Journal of Drug and Alcohol Abuse, 15,* 13–29.

Wikler, A. (1948). Recent progress in research on the neurophysiological basis of morphine addiction. *American Journal of Psychiatry, 105,* 329–338.

Wilkinson, D. A., & Sanchez-Craig, M. (1981). Relevance of brain dysfunction to treatment objectives: Should alcohol-related cognitive deficits influence the way we think about treatment? *Addictive Behaviors, 6,* 253–260.

Wills, T. A., Baker, E., & Botvin, G. J. (1989). Dimensions of assertiveness: Differential relationships to substance abuse in early adolescence. *Journal of Consulting and Clinical Psychology, 57,* 473–478.

Wilsnack, S. C. (1976). The impact of sex-roles on women's alcohol use and abuse. In M. Greenblatt & M. A. Schuckit (Eds.), *Alcohol problems in women and children* (pp. 37–63). New York: Grune & Stratton.

Wilson, G. T. (1987). Cognitive studies in alcoholism. *Journal of Consulting and Clinical Psychology, 55,* 325–331.

Wing, R. R., & Jeffery, R. (1978). Successful losers: A descriptive analysis of the process of weight reduction. *Obesity and Bariatric Medicine, 7,* 190–191.

Woody, G. E., McLellan, A. T., Luborsky, L., & O'Brien, C. P. (1985). Sociopathy and psychotherapy outcome. *Archives of General Psychiatry, 42,* 1081–1086.

Wooley, S. C., & Wooley O. W. (1981). Overeating as substance abuse. *Advances in Substance Abuse, 2,* 41–67.

Yeary, J. R., & Heck, C. L. (1989). Dual diagnosis: Eating disorders and psychoactive substance abuse. *Journal of Psychoactive Drugs, 21,* 239–249.

Young, E. B. (1990). The role of incest issues in relapse. *Journal of Psychoactive Drugs, 22,* 249–258.

Zackon, F. N. (1988). Relapse and "re-joyment": Observations and reflections. In D. Daley (Ed.), *Relapse: Conceptual, research and clinical perspectives* (pp. 67–78). New York: Haworth Press.

Zackon, F., McAuliffe, W. E., & Ch'ien, J. M. N. (1985). *Addict aftercare: A manual of training and self-help* (DHHS Publication No. ADM 85-1341). Washington, DC: U.S. Government Printing Office.

Zaitz, D. (1989, January). Are you an exercise addict? *IDEA Today,* 41–45.

Zimberg, S. (1985). Psychosocial treatment of elderly alcoholics. In S. Zimberg, J. Wallace, & S. B. Blume (Eds.), *Practical approaches to alcoholism psychotherapy* (2nd ed., pp. 347–363). New York: Plenum Press.

Zimmerman, R. S., Warheit, G. J., Ulbrich, P. M., & Auth J. B. (1990). The relationship between alcohol use and attempts and success at smoking cessation. *Addictive Behaviors, 15,* 197–207.

Zucker, R. A., & Gomberg, E. S. L. (1986). Etiology of alcoholism reconsidered: The case for a biopsychosocial process. *American Psychologist, 41,* 783–793.

Zuckerman, M. (1979). *Sensation seeking: Beyond the optimal level of arousal.* Hillsdale, NJ: Lawrence Erlbaum Associates.

Zuckerman, M. (1986). Sensation seeking and the endogenous deficit theory of drug abuse. In S. Szara (Ed.), *Neurobiology of behavioral control in drug abuse* (DHHS Publication No. ADM 87-1506, pp. 59–70). Washington, DC: U.S. Government Printing Office.

Appendix A

Relapse Timeline

Instructions: Place an X in any box representing an abstinent period from *all* substances. Place a Y in any box representing an abstinent period from your primary substance. Place a Z in any box representing a period during which you were involved with either Alcoholics Anonymous, Narcotics Anonymous, or formal treatment.

	1986	1987	1988	1989	1990
January					
February					
March					
April					
May					
June					
July					
August					
September					
October					
November					
December					

Appendix B

Resource List

Annis, H. M., & Davis, C. S. (1989). Relapse prevention. In R. K. Hester & W. R. Miller (Eds.), *Handbook of alcoholism treatment approaches* (pp. 170–182). Elmsford, NY: Pergamon Press. This chapter describes the practical use of the Inventory of Drinking Situations and Situational Confidence Questionnaire.

Burns, D. D. (1989). *The feeling good handbook.* New York: William Morrow. This book builds on the sound cognitive therapy principles of the author's 1980 book, *Feeling Good.* There are numerous cognitive exercises that can be easily adapted to addiction treatment.

Bornstein, P. H., & Bornstein, M. T. (1986). *Marital therapy: A behavioral-communications approach.* Elmsford, NY: Pergamon Press. These authors apply problem-solving and communications skills training to couples. They support their techniques with numerous case examples.

Chaney, E. F. (1989). Social skills training. In R. K. Hester & W. R. Miller (Eds.), *Handbook of alcoholism treatment approaches* (pp. 206–221). Elmsford, NY: Pergamon Press. This chapter provides practical social skills guidelines to different types of interpersonal and intrapersonal situations.

D'Zurilla, T. J. (1986). *Problem-solving therapy: A social competence approach to clinical intervention.* New York: Springer. This book highlights the practical use of problem-solving principles and can be applied to addicted populations.

Friedman, M., & Ulmer, D. (1984). *Treating type A behavior and your heart.* New York: Alfred A Knopf. Written from the standpoint of prevention of heart disease, this self-help book describes techniques that help increase relaxation and develop an even tempo in life.

Gorski, T. T., & Miller, M. (1986). *Staying sober: A guide for relapse prevention.* Independence, MO: Independence Press. This relapse-prevention guide for the recovering person is written as a 12-step program. It can be used as a component of bibliotherapy.

Ludwig, A. M. (1988). *Understanding the alcoholic's mind: The nature of craving and how to control it.* New York: Oxford University Press. This author lets his readers look into the workings of the alcoholic's mind. He reviews cognitive methods for dealing with craving.

Marlatt, G. A., & Gordon, J. R. (Eds.). (1985). *Relapse prevention: Maintenance strategies in the treatment of addictive behavior.* New York: Guilford Press. This "Bible" of relapse prevention, describes Marlatt's cognitive-behavioral model. Techniques for coping with the abstinence violation effect, avoiding apparently irrelevant decisions, and improving lifestyle management are especially useful.

Monti, P. M., Abrams, D. B., Kadden, R. M., & Cooney, N. L. (1989). *Treating alcohol dependence.* New York: Guilford Press. These authors apply the coping skills approach to both inpatient and outpatient treatment. They provide a set of written exercises aimed at enhancing social support, improving communication, and coping with negative feelings.

Moos, R. H., Finney, J. W., & Cronkite, R. C. (1990). *Alcoholism treatment: Context, process, and outcome.* New York: Oxford University Press. Although not a treatment guide, this book reviews key psychosocial variables that need to be considered as part of any addiction treatment.

Rimmele, C. T., Miller, W. R., & Dougher, M. J. (1989). Aversion therapies. In R. K. Hester & W. R. Miller (Eds.), *Handbook of alcoholism treatment approaches* (pp. 128–140). Elmsford, NY: Pergamon Press. This chapter describes the main considerations in covert sensitization with alcoholics.

Shaffer, H. J., & Jones, S. B. (1989). *Quitting cocaine: The struggle against impulse.* Lexington, MA: Lexington Books. This book provides an excellent review of methods by which cocaine addicts remit spontaneously. The authors apply these insights to clinical practice.

Washton, A. M. (1989). *Cocaine addiction: Treatment, recovery, and relapse prevention.* New York: W W Norton. This book applies relapse prevention principles to cocaine treatment, both within the individual and family contexts.

Appendix C

Consequences Form

Instructions: List the positive and negative effects of drugs and alcohol in the spaces below. In the spaces to the right, estimate the percentage of time that you experienced these effects while under the influence. Finally, ask a person who is familiar with your addictive patterns to give his or her own estimates of these percentages.

| | Consequence | | | |
	Positive	*Negative*	*Your %*	*Other %*
Physical				
Psychological				
Relationships				
Legal				
Financial				
Occupational				

Appendix D

Relapse Contract

I realize that my recovery takes a lot of commitment, but that I cannot do it alone. It is important for me to develop a plan in case I lapse so that the episode does not develop into a relapse. This contract is an agreement between my (friend / sponsor / counselor / spouse / coworker / family member) and me. It specifies the steps that each of us will take should I return to alcohol or drug use, even for a short time. I, _____, have discussed with _____, what each of us will do within 24 hours of *any* alcohol or drug use by me. I will take responsibility for the following:

1. Get out of the substance-using situation.
2. Contact a straight person who knows me well.
3. Discuss my lapse/relapse with this person.
4. Review my behaviors, feelings, or thoughts leading up to the lapse/relapse.
5. Use this information to make appropriate improvements in my recovery plan.

_____ agrees to do the following:

1. Assist me in getting into a "safe" situation.
2. Not judge, criticize, or insult me.
4. Not enable me or make excuses for my behavior.
3. Help me determine my mistakes and make suggestions to overcome them.
4. Continue giving constructive feedback about my recovery plan.

_____ Your Signature
_____ Cosigner
_____ Date

Appendix E

Relapse Debriefing Checklist

Instructions: The following questions concern your recent lapse/relapse. Please consider each one carefully.

When did the lapse/relapse happen? _____ What time did it happen? _____

Where were you when you drank or used drugs?

_____ Home _____ Work _____ Car _____ Friend's house

_____ Relative's house _____ School _____ Restaurant/bar

_____ Other

What were you doing?

_____ Socializing _____ Working _____ Engaging in activity

_____ Doing nothing _____ Eating _____ Watching television

_____ Listening to music _____ Other

Were you alone? _____ If not, whom were you with? _____

What were they doing?

_____ Socializing _____ Working _____ Engaging in activity

_____ Doing nothing _____ Eating _____ Watching television

_____ Listening to music _____ Using alcohol/drugs _____ Other

How did you get the alcohol or drugs?

_____ Bought it _____ Found it _____ Offered by others

_____ Asked someone for it _____ Other

How were you feeling immediately before you used the alcohol/drugs?

_____ Happy _____ Sad _____ Relaxed _____ Angry

_____ Frustrated _____ Confused _____ Nervous _____ Guilty

What thought was going through your mind just before you used the alcohol/drugs? _____

What was the major factor that led you to use the alcohol/drugs?
_____

Did you anticipate that you would be using alcohol/drugs in this situation? _____ yes _____ no

How did you feel after this episode was over?

_____ Happy _____ Guilty _____ Relieved _____ Depressed

_____ Confused _____ Angry _____ Shameful _____ Nervous

How likely is it that you will encounter this situation again?

_____ Very unlikely

_____ Unlikely

_____ Somewhat likely

_____ Likely

_____ Very likely

How would you handle this situation if you could do it all over?

_____

Note: This form is adapted from the "Relapse Debriefing Form" presented by Saul Schiffman in Schiffman, S. (1988). Behavioral assessment. In D. M. Donovan & G. A. Marlatt (Eds.), *Assessment of addictive behaviors.* New York: Guilford Press.

Author Index

Subject Index

156

About the Author

Emil J. Chiauzzi, Ph.D., is a senior psychologist with Northeast Psychiatric Associates and Brookside Hospital in Nashua, New Hampshire. He received his doctorate in clinical psychology from the State University of New York at Albany in 1981 and completed an internship at Hutchings Psychiatric Center in Syracuse, New York. He has published in the areas of behavior therapy and substance abuse, with a primary focus on relapse prevention. He also conducts workshops in relapse prevention and other topics related to the addictions.

Psychology Practitioner Guidebooks

Editors
Arnold P. Goldstein, Syracuse University
Leonard Krasner, Stanford University & SUNY at Stony Brook
Sol L. Garfield, Washington University in St. Louis

Elsie M. Pinkston & Nathan L. Linsk—CARE OF THE ELDERLY:
A Family Approach

Donald Meichenbaum—STRESS INOCULATION TRAINING

Sebastiano Santostefano—COGNITIVE CONTROL THERAPY WITH
CHILDREN AND ADOLESCENTS

Lillie Weiss, Melanie Katzman & Sharlene Wolchik—TREATING BULIMIA:
A Psychoeducational Approach

Edward B. Blanchard & Frank Andrasik—MANAGEMENT OF CHRONIC
HEADACHES: A Psychological Approach

Raymond G. Romanczyk—CLINICAL UTILIZATION OF
MICROCOMPUTER TECHNOLOGY

Philip H. Bornstein & Marcy T. Bornstein—MARITAL THERAPY:
A Behavioral-Communications Approach

Michael T. Nietzel & Ronald C. Dillehay—PSYCHOLOGICAL
CONSULTATION IN THE COURTROOM

Elizabeth B. Yost, Larry E. Beutler, M. Anne Corbishley & James R.
Allender—GROUP COGNITIVE THERAPY: A Treatment Approach for
Depressed Older Adults

Lillie Weiss—DREAM ANALYSIS IN PSYCHOTHERAPY

Edward A. Kirby & Liam K. Grimley—UNDERSTANDING AND
TREATING ATTENTION DEFICIT DISORDER

Jon Eisenson—LANGUAGE AND SPEECH DISORDERS IN CHILDREN

Eva L. Feindler & Randolph B. Ecton—ADOLESCENT ANGER
CONTROL: Cognitive-Behavioral Techniques

Michael C. Roberts—PEDIATRIC PSYCHOLOGY: Psychological
Interventions and Strategies for Pediatric Problems

Daniel S. Kirschenbaum, William G. Johnson & Peter M. Stalonas, Jr.—
TREATING CHILDHOOD AND ADOLESCENT OBESITY

W. Stewart Agras—EATING DISORDERS: Management of Obesity,
Bulimia and Anorexia Nervosa

Ian H. Gotlib & Catherine A. Colby—TREATMENT OF DEPRESSION:
An Interpersonal Systems Approach

Walter B. Pryzwansky & Robert N. Wendt—PSYCHOLOGY AS A
PROFESSION: Foundations of Practice

Cynthia D. Belar, William W. Deardorff & Karen E. Kelly—THE
PRACTICE OF CLINICAL HEALTH PSYCHOLOGY

Paul Karoly & Mark P. Jensen—MULTIMETHOD ASSESSMENT OF
CHRONIC PAIN

William L. Golden, E. Thomas Dowd & Fred Friedberg—
HYPNOTHERAPY: A Modern Approach

Patricia Lacks—BEHAVIORAL TREATMENT FOR PERSISTENT INSOMNIA

Arnold P. Goldstein & Harold Keller—AGGRESSIVE BEHAVIOR:
Assessment and Intervention

C. Eugene Walker, Barbara L. Bonner & Keith L. Kaufman—
THE PHYSICALLY AND SEXUALLY ABUSED CHILD: Evaluation
and Treatment

Robert E. Becker, Richard G. Heimberg & Alan S. Bellack—SOCIAL
SKILLS TRAINING TREATMENT FOR DEPRESSION

Richard F. Dangel & Richard A. Polster—TEACHING CHILD
MANAGEMENT SKILLS

Albert Ellis, John F. McInerney, Raymond DiGiuseppe & Raymond J. Yeager—
RATIONAL-EMOTIVE THERAPY WITH ALCOHOLICS AND
SUBSTANCE ABUSERS

Johnny L. Matson & Thomas H. Ollendick—ENHANCING CHILDREN'S
SOCIAL SKILLS: Assessment and Training

Edward B. Blanchard, John E. Martin & Patricia M. Dubbert—NON-DRUG
TREATMENTS FOR ESSENTIAL HYPERTENSION

Samuel M. Turner & Deborah C. Beidel—TREATING OBSESSIVE-
COMPULSIVE DISORDER

Alice W. Pope, Susan M. McHale & W. Edward Craighead—SELF-
ESTEEM ENHANCEMENT WITH CHILDREN AND ADOLESCENTS

Jean E. Rhodes & Leonard A. Jason—PREVENTING SUBSTANCE
ABUSE AMONG CHILDREN AND ADOLESCENTS

Gerald D. Oster, Janice E. Caro, Daniel R. Eagen & Margaret A. Lillo—
ASSESSING ADOLESCENTS

Robin C. Winkler, Dirck W. Brown, Margaret van Keppel & Amy
Blanchard—CLINICAL PRACTICE IN ADOPTION

Roger Poppen—BEHAVIORAL RELAXATION TRAINING AND
ASSESSMENT

Michael D. LeBow—ADULT OBESITY THERAPY

Robert Paul Liberman, Kim T. Mueser & William J. DeRisi —SOCIAL
SKILLS TRAINING FOR PSYCHIATRIC PATIENTS

Johnny L. Matson—TREATING DEPRESSION IN CHILDREN AND
ADOLESCENTS

Sol L. Garfield—THE PRACTICE OF BRIEF PSYCHOTHERAPY

Arnold P. Goldstein, Barry Glick, Mary Jane Irwin, Claudia Pask-McCartney
& Ibrahim Rubama—REDUCING DELINQUENCY: Intervention in
the Community

Albert Ellis, Joyce L. Sichel, Raymond J. Yeager, Dominic J. DiMattia,
& Raymond DiGiuseppe—RATIONAL-EMOTIVE COUPLES THERAPY

Clive R. Hollin—COGNITIVE-BEHAVIORAL INTERVENTIONS WITH
YOUNG OFFENDERS

Margaret P. Korb, Jeffrey Gorrell & Vernon Van De Riet—GESTALT
THERAPY: Practice and Theory, Second Edition

Donald A. Williamson—ASSESSMENT OF EATING DISORDERS:
Obesity, Anorexia, and Bulimia Nervosa